WEATHER

WEATHER

THE NATURE OF WEATHER
CHANGES FROM DAY TO DAY

By

The Hon. RALPH ABERCROMBY

New Edition, revised and largely rewritten,
by

A. H. R. GOLDIE
M.A., F.R.S.E.

LONDON
KEGAN PAUL, TRENCH, TRUBNER & CO., LTD.
BROADWAY HOUSE: 68-74 CARTER LANE, E.C. 4
1934

PRINTED IN GREAT BRITAIN BY
STEPHEN AUSTIN AND SONS, LTD., HERTFORD

CONTENTS

CONTENTS

ILLUSTRATIONS

ix

PREFACE

The object of this work is to place before the general reader a short but clear picture of the science of which it treats.

In its original form the work was issued in 1887 under the authorship of the Hon. Ralph Abercromby, whose early death, in 1897, has been described as " an irreparable loss to meteorological science ". The book passed, without change, through seven editions, attaining a distinguished place in the literature of the science and becoming the basis and inspiration of many textbooks in this and other countries.

In accepting the invitation of the publishers to prepare a new edition I have endeavoured to keep the original object in view, " to sketch the great principles of the science as a whole, and to give a clear picture of the general conclusions as to the actual nature of weather to which meteorologists have been led."

The advances of forty-six years have been such that the work has had to be largely rewritten, yet some part of the original plan may be seen and certain portions of the original work, chiefly in two chapters, have for good reasons been incorporated again with as little change as possible.

This new edition must be expected to differ from its forerunners in containing an account of present day knowledge of the upper air and in the prominence given at every stage to the application of physical principles in explaining the processes of weather.

A good deal of modern theory and certain broad generalizations have been introduced ; this is not from any exaggerated idea as to the finality of the theory ; but rather because of the powerful assistance offered by a theory when one is attempting to form a connected picture of the results so far derived from the vast accumulation of observational material.

Bibliographies appear at the ends of some of the chapters, the references therein being to matters which though perhaps mentioned in the text, have been treated incompletely. The references are given for the convenience of readers who may wish to explore such matters further, and the selection has been governed by this consideration.

In the case of matters which have been treated in a fairly complete manner in the text references to original papers have not as a rule been given, though in numerous cases the names of authorities have been mentioned.

I am indebted to the Controller of H.M. Stationery Office for permission to reproduce Figs. 29, 34, 35, 45, and 68 taken from official publications of the Meteorological Office, and to the Director of the Meteorological Office for the loan of blocks for these and for Fig. 69, and for permission to reproduce the autographic records in Fig. 31 and the weather chart in Fig. 57. For permission to publish Fig. 69 I am indebted to Leading Aircraftsman R. Pleasants, of the Royal Air Force, Peshawar, who took the original photograph. Certain other figures and some of the tables are based on material which has appeared in official publications of the Meteorological Office.

For the original prints of the cloud photographs reproduced in Figs. 12 to 21, I am indebted to Mr. G. A. Clarke, of the Observatory, King's College, Aberdeen, and for the photographs in Figs. 22 and 23 to Professor Carl Störmer, of the University of Oslo.

A. H. R. GOLDIE.

EDINBURGH.
November, 1933.

WEATHER

CHAPTER I

INTRODUCTORY

AT an early stage among every people the premonitory signs of good or bad weather become formulated into short sayings or popular prognostics. Many of these are still current in every part of the world, but their quality and value are very varied. Some represent the astrological attitude of mind by referring weather changes to the influence of the stars or phases of the moon ; some, on the contrary, have a value, at least in conjunction with other aids to weather forecasting.

In many cases these prognostics were found to come true and in some they failed, but no explanation could be suggested ; neither could any reason be given why the same weather was not always preceded by the same signs. A halo sometimes precedes a storm ; why does it not always do so ? Why is rain sometimes preceded by a soft sky and sometimes by hard clouds? When the observation of weather developed gradually on more scientific lines it became possible to appreciate correctly the uses and the limitations of the popular prognostics.

THE BAROMETER

The invention of the barometer by Torricelli (1608–1647) made it possible to measure atmospheric pressure. The air is held to the earth, just as water or any other substance is, by its weight. The barometric pressure at any spot is the weight of air overlying that spot. The pressure is very considerable and we are only òblivious of it

B

because it exists everywhere. Actually if all or nearly all the air is removed from a closed vessel, the vessel if not very strongly constructed will collapse under the outside pressure. The average pressure at sea level is about $14\frac{3}{4}$ lb. per square inch, or a ton per square foot. It is sufficient to balance a column of mercury nearly 30 inches high, and the mercury barometer is in effect an instrument for balancing the weight of the atmosphere and measuring it in terms of the length of a column of mercury. It seems somewhat illogical to measure a pressure in terms of a length, but as a practical method it has survived and atmospheric pressures in the English-speaking countries have commonly been expressed in inches, whilst in those countries which have adopted the metric system the pressures have been expressed in millimetres. The objection to such a system is that the length is not a measure of the atmospheric pressure until the density of the mercury, the temperature of the scale, and the value of gravity at the place have been allowed for. Therefore in scientific meteorology a rational pressure unit has come into use—the millibar. Actually the absolute unit of pressure on the centimetre-gramme-second system is the dyne, i.e. a pressure equal to the weight of one gramme on each square centimetre of area. A million dynes, which is roughly the average pressure of the atmosphere at sea level, is called a bar. It has been found convenient in meteorology to use the millibar or thousandth part of a bar as the unit of pressure, and this became the standard in the British Meteorological Office in 1914. A pressure of 1,000 mb. is equivalent to 29·53 inches of mercury, or roughly it is about the point where we are accustomed to see " change " in the conventional descriptions engraved on barometers. In parts of the second and thirteenth chapters of this book, which stand very much in the classical form in which they were written by Abercromby in 1887, pressures are expressed in inches. In some other parts millibars or both millibars and inches are used. The average value of barometric pressure at mean sea level in the British Isles is 29·92 mercury inches or 1013·2 millibars. The extremes recorded in these islands are 27·33 inches or 925·5 millibars, on the one hand, at Ochtertyre, Perthshire, on 26th January, 1884, and 31·11 inches or 1053·5 millibars on the other hand.

Since the barometric pressure on any area is the weight of air overlying that area, it follows that for every thousand feet (say) of ascent in the atmosphere the pressure must decrease by an amount equivalent to the weight of that depth of air. It will be shown later on in the book that if we know the temperature of the air at different levels and the pressure at ground level, we can by successive steps calculate the manner in which pressure diminishes, with increase of height. On the average the rate of decrease for the first few thousand feet is about 1 inch of mercury per 1,000 feet, or about 115 millibars per kilometre.

Since barometric readings depend so largely on the altitude at which they are made, it follows that if we wish to compare the readings at various places we must first make due allowance or adjustment for the difference of level. The most practical way of doing so is to " reduce " all readings to some standard level, usually Mean Sea Level.

Very soon after the invention of the barometer, observation showed that, in a general way, the pressure fell before rain and wind, and rose for finer weather ; also that bad weather was more common when the barometer was low, independent of its motion one way or the other, than when the level was high. But as with prognostics, so with these indications, many failures occurred. Sometimes rain would fall with a high or rising barometer, and sometimes it would be fine with a very low or falling barometer. No reason could be given at that time for these apparent exceptions.

TEMPERATURE AND HUMIDITY

It cannot be said that even so much success attended early efforts to explain or to forecast weather on the basis of the temperature and humidity of the air as observed at any single station. It was found that the air always contained a certain amount of moisture in the form of invisible vapour and means were invented for measuring this amount accurately. From this, the conditions of the formation of dew and visible cloud were discovered, and it was noted also that before many cases of rain the air became more charged with vapour. This latter fact gave the explanation of several rain-prognostics, but along these lines beyond this point no advance was made. Many cases of rain could not be shown by any means to be associated with an increase of moisture, at least at the heights accessible to measurement. Sometimes rain fell after a relatively dry air and some explanation was in any case needed to account for the very variable quantity of moisture in the air from time to time.

It was not the physics, however, that was at fault but the manner of its application, the idea that continuous observation of the atmosphere at one place could solve the problem of weather in the same relatively simple way that study of a specimen of a gas in a laboratory can elucidate its physical and chemical properties. The idea has died hard, if indeed it has yet died. The truth is that the whole world is the meteorologist's laboratory, that he cannot isolate specimens and control experiments. Whilst he makes observations in one place, entirely new conditions, developed in some other part of the globe, are travelling towards him. These matters will be explained more fully later ; in the meantime we make some remarks about temperature and the units used.

The temperature of the air is usually obtained from the readings of mercury or spirit thermometers, protected from the direct action of the sun or the radiation of any bodies hotter or colder than the air itself, but at the same time so exposed that the air may flow freely over the thermometers. Fundamentally, therefore, some form of louvred screen or ventilated box forms the appropriate container for a thermometer. In this country the Stevenson screen has received official approval.

The temperature scales in most frequent use are the

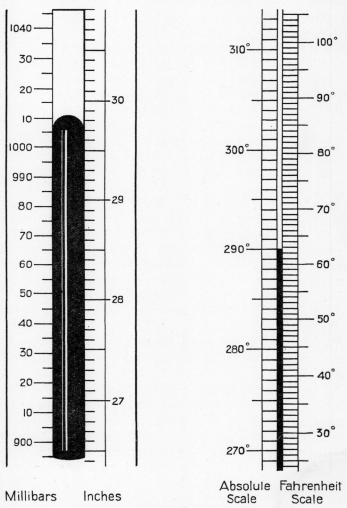

Millibars   Inches   Absolute Fahrenheit
                                Scale   Scale

FIG. 1.—Pressure and Temperature Scales.

Fahrenheit (F), Centigrade (C), and Absolute (A) scales. For ordinary purposes the first is used largely in the English-speaking countries and the second in most other countries. The relationship between these scales is determinable from the features that freezing point of water, commonly known as freezing point, is 32° F or 0° C or 273° A, whilst boiling point (at " normal " atmospheric pressure) is 212° F or 100° C or 373° A. Thus the degrees on the last two scales are equal, though the scales start from points differing by 273 degrees, whilst a step of 5 degrees on either of the two last is equivalent to a step of 9 degrees on the first scale. The Fahrenheit scale has the advantage that its degree is of convenient size for many meteorological purposes, so that decimals need scarcely be used and that the great majority of all air temperatures ordinarily experienced can be expressed in two figures. Both the Fahrenheit and the Centigrade scales have the disadvantage that negative temperatures do occur—much more frequently, of course, on the Centigrade scale—and that without modification they are inconvenient for use in physical calculations. For the last mentioned purpose and for the expression of air temperatures at all heights without introducing negative values the Absolute scale is appropriate. In this work the Fahrenheit scale will be used chiefly and unless otherwise stated.

We introduce in Fig. 1 a diagram showing how the pressure scales are related to one another and how the temperature scales are related.

All that need be said about the measurement of humidity is that in practice the humidity of the air is most commonly determined either from comparative readings of dry and wet bulb thermometers, or from the indications of a recording instrument known as a hair hygrograph. The first device depends on the fact that evaporation lowers the temperature of any surface from which it is taking place and that the more humid the air the less the rate of evaporation. The second device depends on the fact that the length of a hair varies according to its humidity and it is therefore possible to arrange a bunch of hairs to operate a recording instrument.

RAINFALL

In the British Isles and in most English-speaking countries rainfall is most commonly measured in inches and hundredths of an inch. The millimetre is also in use as a unit of measurement. The relationship between the two systems is that—

$$1 \text{ mm.} = \cdot04 \text{ in.}$$
$$\text{or } 1 \text{ in.} = 25 \cdot 4 \text{ mm.}$$

WIND

Wind direction is commonly expressed according to the points of the compass, but true or geographical, not magnetic north, is used as the starting point. Alternatively the direction is expressed in degrees measured from true north, through east, south, and west. Thus N.E. is equivalent to 45°, E. to 90°, W. to 270°.

Wind speeds when measured instrumentally are expressed commonly in miles per hour or metres per second ; a speed of 1 metre per second being equivalent to one of 2·2 miles per hour. When speed is not measured instrumentally, the wind force is estimated according to the Beaufort Scale to which reference is made in the next chapter.

STATISTICS

The science of probabilities came into existence about the commencement of last century and developed the science of statistics. The average readings of meteorological instruments, such as the barometer or thermometer, or such observations as the mean direction and force of the wind, at any number of places, were summarized and the results were plotted on charts so as to show the distribution of mean pressure, temperature, etc., over the world. By this means a great advance was made. These charts conclusively showed that many meteorological elements hitherto considered capricious in their variation were really controlled by general causes, such as the distribution of land and sea.

Still more fruitful were these charts as the parents of the more modern methods of plotting, for large areas, the readings of the barometer, etc., at a given hour, instead of the mean value for a month or a year. Again, the tabulation of the relative frequency of different winds at sea enabled many ocean voyages—notably those across the " doldrums " or belt of calms and light airs near the Equator—to be materially shortened.

Statistics also of the annual amount of rainfall became of commercial value as bearing on questions of the economic supply of water for large towns, and valuable information was acquired as to the dependence of mortality on different kinds of weather. Of more purely scientific interest were the variations of pressure, temperature, wind, etc., depending on the time of day, or what are technically known as diurnal variations, which were brought to light by these comparisons.

When attempt was made to apply statistics to weather changes from day to day, it was found that average results were useless. The mean temperature for any particular day of the year might be 50° F, if deduced from the returns of a great many years, but in any particular year it might be as low as 40° F or as high as 60° F. The first application of the method was made by Napoleon Bonaparte, who requested Laplace to calculate when the cold set in severely over Russia. The latter found that on the average it did not set in hard till January. The Emperor made his plans accordingly ; a sharp spell of cold came in December, and the army was lost.

It has now been recognized that average values, though giving some representation of climate, give little or no guide to weather and particularly to future weather, especially in the temperate zones where variety is the prominent feature. Information about the relative frequency of occurrence of various conditions takes us a little further.

SYNOPTIC CHARTS

In the early part of the nineteenth century the idea had been gaining ground of the " travel of weather ", or of forecasting the weather of the future at a given place from consideration of a map of the weather of the present over a wide area. With the introduction of the electric telegraph this idea of a " synoptic " picture became a practical one and in 1849 in England and in America experiments were carried out. These experiments, together with the effects of various disasters at sea (arising from gales which it seemed could have been forecasted), led to the establishment about 1854 of Meteorological Offices in England and France and later on in other countries. The synoptic method of studying data has changed the whole aspect of meteorology. The earliest weather chart in meteorological history was one prepared by Brandes and related to the distribution of pressure and wind in Europe on 6th March, 1783.

PLAN OF THE BOOK

A vast amount of work has been given to synoptic meteorology in all parts of the world, and the object of this book is to supply a short account of the principal results which have been discovered by means of synoptic charts, or by the interpretation of statistics with the help of such charts. British weather will be dealt with more largely.

The book will commence with a chapter introducing some of the simpler portions of synoptic meteorology and the idea of travel of weather. In this part (Chapter II) the prognostic aspect will predominate, and the ideas as developed up to the time when the first edition of this work was published will be largely followed, not only because these ideas are simple and as broad generalizations are excellent, but also because the account in question, as written by Abercromby, is one of the classical portions of meteorological literature, and probably the most quoted, even in modern works on the subject.

It is then considered necessary to devote the third chapter to the upper air and a discussion of physical processes, in order to prepare the ground for succeeding chapters.

Clouds form a chapter by themselves, and here again some attention is devoted to prognostic values. In the fifth chapter we pass to diagnosis of the detailed structure of the cyclone in the vertical direction as well as in the horizontal, and the relation of wind, cloud, and weather to that structure. From this we pass to the consideration of the records of anemographs, barographs, thermographs, and other continuously recording instruments, and show especially how the changes in wind, barometric pressure, temperature, etc., as seen on successive synoptic charts, correspond to the sequence of events as observed in any one place ; this is one of the fundamental points of synoptic meteorology.

We then discuss the relation of the speed and direction of the wind to the isobars and after that the manner in which the distribution of heat and cold from day to day and in various parts of the world is effected.

In the ninth and tenth chapters the study of diurnal and local effects enables us to introduce the idea of maps of normal values and to indicate how the statistics have an interpretation in physical principles. The eleventh chapter deals with line squalls and thunderstorms and generally with the class of phenomena in which instability of the arrangement of masses of atmosphere either in the vertical or horizontal directions plays an important part.

The twelfth chapter by way of preparation for the thirteenth deals with the place of European weather in the general circulation of the atmosphere over the globe. The thirteenth chapter deals with the important matter of types and spells of weather. Here again, though with some changes and additions, we include a part of Abercromby's original work, which seems to have gained a lasting place in meteorological literature.

The fourteenth chapter is concerned with the longer period variations of weather, seasonal and annual, and the questions of recurrences and weather cycles.

The fifteenth chapter deals with visibility and fog, and the sixteenth with that class of storms in which more or less violent rotational motion is the predominant feature, namely tornadoes and tropical revolving storms.

Finally, in the last chapter, we give an outline of the official and international organization for synoptic meteorology and mention some practical applications.

BIBLIOGRAPHY

The Observer's Handbook. London: H.M. Stationery Office. Price 5s.
The Meteorological Glossary. London: H.M. Stationery Office. Price 4s. 6d.

Chapter II

SYNOPTIC CHARTS

Introduction

THE data required for the construction of synoptic charts are the readings of any instrument (say the barometer), or any observations on the sky or the weather (say where rain is falling, or cloud or blue sky is seen), at a large number of places at the same moment (say 7 a.m. G.M.T.). A map of the area or district from which the observations have been received is then taken, the barometer-readings (all duly " reduced " to Mean Sea Level) are marked down over their respective places, and then lines are drawn through all the places where the pressure is equal, for instance, through all the places where the pressure is 29·9 inches, and again at convenient intervals, say 29·7 inches, 29·5 inches, and so on. These lines are called isobars—that is, lines of equal atmospheric weight or pressure. This method of showing the distribution of pressure by isobars is exactly analogous to that of marking out hills and valleys by means of contour lines of equal altitude.

Similarly the places which report rain, cloud, blue sky, etc., are marked with convenient symbols to denote these phenomena. In Great Britain a code of letters is in use which was originally introduced by Admiral Sir Francis Beaufort. Some additions have been made to the original schedule, and it now stands as follows :—

b   blue sky, whether with clear or hazy atmosphere.
bc   sky partly cloudy.
c   cloudy, i.e. detached opening clouds.
d   drizzle.
e   wet air without rain falling, a copious deposit of water on trees or buildings.

f   fog.

fe   wet fog.

g   gloom.

h   hail.

l   lightning.

m   mist ; range of visibility 1,100 yards or more, but less than 2,200 yards.

o   overcast, i.e. the whole sky covered with one impervious cloud.

p   passing showers.

q   squalls.

KQ   line squall.

r   rain.

rs   sleet, i.e. rain and snow together.

s   snow.

t   thunder.

tl   thunderstorm.

u   ugly, threatening sky.

v   unusual visibility of distant objects.

w   dew.

x   hoar frost.

y   dry air (less than 60 per cent humidity).

z   haze ; range of visibility 1,100 yards or more, but less than 2,200 yards.

To denote great intensity of any phenomenon a capital letter is used and to denote slight intensity a small suffix $_o$ is added. Continuity is indicated by repetition of the letter and intermittence by prefixing the letter i. Thus we have :—

R   heavy rain.

r   moderate rain.

r_o slight rain.

RR   continuous heavy rain.

rr   continuous moderate rain.

ir_o intermittent slight rain.

Then arrows are placed over each observing station, with a number of barbs and feathers which indicate the force of the wind. By an international convention, the arrows always fly with the wind ; that is to say, they do not face the wind like the pointer of a wind vane. The scale of force usually adopted is one put forward by Admiral Beaufort so long ago as 1806 ; it was based on the amount of canvas a man-of-war could carry under certain conditions. In the table below Beaufort's original specification has been replaced by one

TABLE I
BEAUFORT SCALE OF WIND FORCE WITH PROBABLE EQUIVALENTS OF THE NUMBERS OF THE SCALE

Beaufort Number	Beaufort's description of wind (International)	Specification of Beaufort Scale for use on land, based on observations made at land stations	Equivalent speed in miles per hour at 33 feet above ground
0	Calm	Smoke rises vertically.	0
1	Light air	Direction of wind shown by smoke drift, but not by wind vanes .	2
2	Light breeze	Wind felt on face ; leaves rustle ; ordinary vane moved by wind	5
3	Gentle breeze	Leaves and small twigs in constant motion ; wind extends light flag . .	10
4	Moderate breeze	Raises dust and loose paper ; small branches are moved .	15
5	Fresh breeze	Small trees in leaf begin to sway ; crested wavelets form on inland waters	21
6	Strong breeze	Large branches in motion ; whistling heard in telegraph wires	27
7	Moderate gale	Whole trees in motion ; inconvenience felt when walking against wind . . .	35
8	Fresh gale	Breaks twigs off trees ; generally impedes progress . . .	42
9	Strong gale	Slight structural damage occurs (chimney pots and slates removed)	50
10	Whole gale	Seldom experienced inland ; trees uprooted ; considerable structural damage occurs .	59
11	Storm	Very rarely experienced ; accompanied by widespread damage	68
12	Hurricane	. . . . . .	above 75

appropriate to land observations and a scale of equivalent speeds in miles per hour has been added. The equivalents just mentioned refer to the height at which anemometrical records are commonly taken.

When all this is done, we can see at a glance whether or how wind, rain, cloud, and blue sky are connected with the shape of the isobars. In fact, a synoptic chart gives us, as it were, a bird's-eye view of the weather at the particular moment for which the chart is constructed, over the whole district from which reports have been received. Suppose now that after an interval of twenty-four hours another chart is constructed from observations taken over the same area, then we generally find that the shape of the isobars and the position of the areas of high and low pressure have considerably changed, and with them the positions of those areas where the weather is good or bad. For instance, suppose that at 7 a.m. on one morning we find pressure low over Ireland and high over Denmark, with rain over Ireland, cloud over England, and blue sky in Denmark ; and that by 7 a.m. on the following day we find that the low pressure area has advanced to Denmark, that a new high pressure has formed over Ireland, with rain in Denmark, broken sky in England, and blue sky in Ireland ; suppose, too, that the record of the weather, say in London, for those twenty-four hours had been as follows : cloudy sky, followed by rain, after which the sky broke ; how can an inspection of the two charts help us to explain the weather as observed in London during that day ? Our bird's-eye view would show that the rain area which lay over Ireland in the morning had drifted during the day over England, including London, and covered Denmark by next morning. It would also tell us that the position of the rain was identified with, and moved along with the low pressure. This is the fundamental idea of all synoptic meteorology. In looking at the " ups" and " downs " of the barometer when they are marked on a diagram, and then at any two synoptic charts which refer to the same period, it is difficult at first to see any connection. One must learn, however, to make deductions from barograms—as such barometric traces are called— and to relate them to the synoptic charts.

RELATION OF WIND AND WEATHER TO ISOBARS

Many thousands of synoptic charts have been constructed for all parts of the world, and by comparing them the following important generalizations have been arrived at :—

(1) That in general the configuration of the isobars takes one of seven well-defined forms.

(2) That, independent of the shape of the isobars, the wind takes a definite direction relative to the trend of these lines, and the position of the nearest area of low pressure.

(3) That the velocity of the wind is always nearly proportional to the closeness of the isobars.

(4) That the weather—that is to say, the kind of cloud, rain, fog, etc.—at any moment depends on the shape and not the closeness, of the isobars, some shapes being associated with good and others with bad weather.

(5) That the regions thus mapped out by the isobars were constantly shifting their position, so that changes of weather were associated with the drifting past of these areas of good or bad weather, just as on a small scale rain falls as a squall drives by. The motion of these areas was found to follow certain laws, so that forecasting weather changes in advance became a possibility.

(6) That sometimes in the temperate zones, and more often in the tropics, rain fell without any appreciable or very obvious change in the isobars, though the wind more regularly conformed to the general run of these lines.

It will be convenient to take first the broad features of the relation of wind to isobars, which are as follows :—

As regards direction, the wind in all cases is not exactly parallel to the isobar, but inclined towards the lower pressure at an angle of from 30° to 40°. If you stand with your back to the wind, the lowest pressure will always be on your left hand in the northern hemisphere, and on your right in the southern hemisphere. This is what is commonly known as " Buys Ballot's Law ".

As to velocity, all we need to say here is that the velocity is roughly proportional to the closeness of the isobars, and that the measure of the closeness is called the barometric gradient, for in the chapter on wind and calm we shall go into greater detail on this subject.

The upshot of these two principles is, that if you give a meteorologist a chart of the world with the isobars only marked on it, he can put in very approximately the direction and force of the wind all over the globe.

When we have explained the relation of weather to the shapes of the isobars, we shall see that he could also write

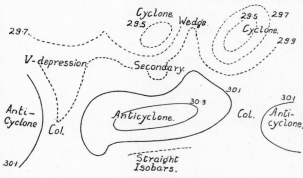

FIG. 2.—The Seven Fundamental Shapes of Isobars.

down very nearly the kind of weather which would be experienced everywhere.

THE SEVEN FUNDAMENTAL SHAPES OF ISOBARS

In Fig. 2 we give in a diagrammatic form the broad features only of the distribution of pressure as it was over the North Atlantic, Europe, and the Eastern portions of the United States on 27th February, 1865.

Coast-lines are omitted so as not to confuse the eye, so also are lines of latitude and longitude ; but the footnote at the bottom of the figure represents the Equator, and the top of the diagram would be on the Arctic Circle.   All

c

pressures of and under 29·9 inches (1012·5 mb.) are shown with dotted lines, so that the eye sees at a glance the broad distribution of high or low pressure. The whole seven fundamental shapes of isobars will be found there.

Looking at the top of the diagram, we see two nearly circular areas of low pressure, round which the isobars are rather closely packed. Such areas, or rather the configurations of isobars which enclose them, are called " cyclones ", from a Greek word meaning circle, because they are nearly circular, and, as we shall see presently, the wind blows nearly in a circle round their centre.

Just south of one of the cyclones, the isobar of 29·9 inches forms a small sort of nearly circular loop, enclosing lower pressure ; this is called a " secondary cyclone ", because it is usually secondary or subsidiary to the primary cyclones above described.

Further to the left the same isobar of 29·9 inches bends itself into the shape of the letter V, also enclosing low pressure ; this is called a " V-shaped depression ", or, shortly, a " V ".

Between the two cyclones the isobar of 29·9 inches projects upwards, like a wedge or an inverted letter V, but this time encloses high pressure ; this shape of lines is called a " wedge ".

Below all these we see an oblong area of high pressure, round which the isobars are very far apart ; this is called an " anticyclone ", because it is the opposite to a cyclone in everything—wind, weather, pressure, etc. The name was introduced by Sir Francis Galton about 1862.

Between every two anticyclones we find a furrow, neck, or " col " of low pressure analogous to the col which forms a pass between two adjacent mountain-peaks.

Lastly, as marked in the lower edge of the diagram, isobars sometimes run straight, so that they do not include any kind of area, but represent a barometric slope analogous to the sloping side of a long hill.

We may forestall succeeding chapters so far as to say

that the cyclones, secondaries, V's, and wedges are usually moving towards the east at the rate of about 20 miles an hour ; but that the anticyclones, on the contrary, are frequently stationary for days, and sometimes for months together.

We should also note that, though the general principles of prognostics and the broad features of the weather in each of these shapes of isobars are the same all over the world, the minute details which we intend to give now apply to Great Britain and the temperate zones only.

We shall now take the five more important shapes separately, and detail the kind of wind and weather which is experienced in different parts of each of them. Incidentally we shall give the explanation of the nature of the popular prognostics. The account of " V's " and " cols " will be reserved for the fifth chapter.

CYCLONES

We begin with these as they are the most important. In Fig. 3 there is written in words the kind of weather which would be found in every portion of a typical cyclone ; arrows also show the direction of the wind relative to the isobars and to the centre.

First let us look at the isobars. They are oval, and they are not quite concentric, but the centre of the inner one we shall call the centre of the cyclone. Now observe the numbers attached to the isobars ; the outer one is 30·0 inches, the inner one 29·0 inches. But suppose the outer one was the same, but the inner one was 29·5. We should then have another cyclone, differing from the one illustrated in nothing but depth ; that is in the closeness of the isobars, or the steepness of the barometric slope.

Observation has shown that under these circumstances the general character of the weather and the direction of the wind everywhere would be much the same ; the only difference would be that the wind would blow a hard gale in the first, and only a moderate breeze in the second case ; and that what was a sharp squall in the one would be a quiet shower in the other. This is one of the fundamental principles of synoptic meteorology—that the character of the weather and direction of the wind depend entirely on the shape of the isobars, while the force of the wind and intensity of the character of the weather depend on the closeness of the isobars.

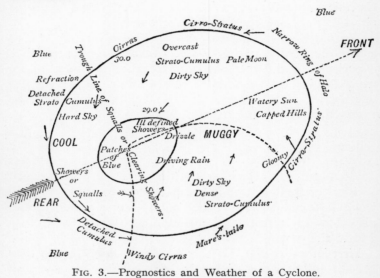

FIG. 3.—Prognostics and Weather of a Cyclone.

The difference in the details of the weather in a cyclone, or any other isobaric shape, which is due to difference in the steepness of the isobars, is called a difference in intensity. Hence, when we speak of a cyclone as being intense, we mean that it has steep isobars somewhere. We shall find that there is no difference between the cyclones which cause storms and those which cause ordinary weather except intensity. This is another of the fundamental principles of meteorology.

Returning now to our cyclone, the whole of the portion

in front of the centre facing the direction towards which it moves is called its front, and the whole of this portion may obviously be divided into a right and left front. The other side of the centre is, of course, the rear of the cyclone. Then, as the whole cyclone moves along its course, it is evident that the barometer will be falling more or less at every portion of the front, and rising more or less everywhere in rear, so that there must be a line of places somewhere across the cyclone, where the barometer has touched its lowest point and is just going to rise. This line is called the " trough " of the cyclone, because if we look at the barometer-trace at any one place the " ups " and " downs " suggest the analogy of waves, so that the lowest part of a trace may be called a " trough ". Or we may look at the cyclone as a circular eddy, moving in a given direction, and so far presenting some analogy to a wave. Here we are faced with the primary difficulty of understanding synoptic charts. When we look at any chart of a cyclone which represents the state of things existing at some one moment, there is little to suggest the idea of a trough, because the latter depends on the motion of a cyclone, which cannot be shown on a chart. Perhaps the following illustration may help to explain the nature of a trough. Suppose the cyclone represented the inside of a conical crater ; if we walked along the line that marks the path of the centre from the word " FRONT " to the word " REAR " on the diagram, we should pass over the centre of the crater, and be walking downhill all the time till we reached the bottom, and uphill afterwards. But now, if we walked across the crater on any other line parallel to this one, say from the word " pale " to the word " COOL ", we shall equally walk downhill till we arrive at the point occupied by the letter q in the word " squalls ". At q we should still be on the side of the crater and some distance from the centre, but after passing q we should begin to walk uphill.

When we have once realized the meaning of the trough,

we shall not fall into the error of thinking that because our barometer has begun to rise, the centre of the cyclone has necessarily passed over us. It is probably only the trough, but we shall explain afterwards how we can tell whether it is the centre or not.

So far for the shape and names of the different portions of the cyclone ; let us now consider the wind. A glance at the arrows will show that, broadly speaking, the wind rotates round the centre in a direction opposite to the motion of the hands of a watch. That is to say, that in the extreme front, following the outer isobar, the wind is from the south-east ; further round it is from the east-north-east ; still further, from the north-north-west ; then from about west ; and, finally, from the south-west. Then we note that in front the wind is slightly incurved towards the centre, and there blows somewhat across the isobars, while in rear it has little or no incurvature, and blows nearly parallel to the isobars. The velocity or force of the wind will depend on the closeness of the isobars. In the diagram they are more closely set in rear than in front of the cyclone and therefore the wind is stronger behind the centre. In Fig. 3 a dotted line has been added which did not appear in the original Abercromby diagram of a cyclone. It will be seen that the line isolates a sector of south-westerly wind. More will be said about this in a later chapter. In another later chapter also we shall have to go much more minutely into the subject of wind, both on the surface and in the upper currents ; but here we wish to confine our attention as far as possible to the weather and appearance of the sky.

The weather in a cyclone is somewhat complicated. Some characteristic features depend on the position of the trough, and have nothing to do with the centre. For instance, the weather and sky over the whole front of the cyclone— that is, all that lies in front of the trough—is characterized by a muggy, oppressive feel of the air, and a dirty, gloomy sky of a stratiform type, whether it is actually raining or only cloudy. On the other side, the whole of the rear is characterized by a sharp, brisk feel of the air, and a hard, firm sky of cumulus type.

But, on the contrary, other characteristic features are related to the centre, and have little to do with the trough. The rotation of the wind, though slightly modified near the trough, is in the main related to the centre, and the broad features of the weather in a cyclone are—a patch of rain near the centre, a ring of cloud surrounding the rain, and blue sky outside the whole system. The centre of the rain-area is rarely concentric with the isobars. It usually extends further in front than in the rear, and more to the south than to the north, but is still primarily related to the centre.

This will be readily seen by reference to the diagram ; there the drizzle and driving rain extend some distance to the right front, while almost directly behind the centre patches of blue sky become visible. Thus a cyclone has, as it were, a double symmetry ; that is to say, one set of phenomena, such as warmth, cloud character, etc., which are roughly symmetrically disposed in front and rear of the trough ; and another set such as wind and rain which are symmetrically arranged round the centre. There is reason to believe that what we may call the circular symmetry of a cyclone is due to the rotation of the air, while the properties which are related to the trough are due to the forward motion of the whole system.

As this is a somewhat difficult conception, perhaps the following analogy may not be out of place. Let us consider the twofold distribution of the population of London. As regards density, we find a comparatively thinly populated district in the centre of London—that is, in the City proper. Round this there is a tolerably symmetrical ring of very densely populated streets, outside of which the population thins away towards the suburbs. But at the same time London is divided into very well-defined halves of comparative poverty and wealth—the east and west ends respectively. This is a far more strongly marked distinction than any which is found between the north and south sides

of London, in spite of a river that might have been supposed
to make a natural boundary. This distinction into an
east and west end is always attributed to the general
march of the population westwards. Thus the front and
rear of the moving population have a symmetry
independent of the density of the population round
a centre.

Prognostic Aspects

Returning now to the details of weather in a cyclone,
we have marked on the diagram the kind of weather and
cloud which would be found in the different parts.
The first thing which will strike us is that the descriptive
epithets applied to the sky contain the phraseology of
the most familiar prognostics. At the extreme front we
see marked " pale moon ", " watery sun ", which means
that in that portion of a cyclone the moon or sun will
look pale or watery through a peculiar kind of sky. But
all over the world a pale moon and watery sun are known
as prognostics of rain. Why are they so ? The reason we
can now explain. Since a cyclone is usually moving,
after the front part where the sky gives a watery look
to the sun has passed over the observer, the rainy portion
will also have to come over him before he experiences
the blue sky on the other side of the cyclone.

Suppose the cyclone stood still for a week, then the
observer would see a watery sky for a week, without any
rain following. Suppose the cyclone came on so far as
to bring him under a watery sky, and then died out or
moved in another direction, then, after the watery
sky no rain would follow, but the sky would clear. The
prognostic would then be said to fail, but the word is
only partially applicable. The watery sky was formed and
was seen by the observer, because he was in the
appropriate portion of the cyclone, and so far the
prognostic told its story correctly, viz. that the observer

was in front of the rainy area of a cyclone. The prognostic failed in its ordinary indication because the cyclone did not move on as usual, but died out, and therefore never brought its rainy portion over the observer. This is the commonest source of the so-called failure of a rain-prognostic in Great Britain. The reason why, on the other hand, all rain is not preceded by a watery sky is because there are other sources of rain besides a cyclone, which are preceded by a different set of weather signs.

The same reasoning which applies to a watery sky holds good for every other cyclone-prognostic. We shall have explained why any prognostic portends rain when we have shown that the kind of sky or other appearance which forms the prognostic belongs to the front of the rainy portion of a cyclone. Conversely we shall have explained why any prognostic indicates finer weather when we have shown that the kind of sky belongs to the rear of a cyclone. It will be convenient, therefore, to describe the weather in different parts of a cyclone, and the appropriate prognostics together.

First we take those prognostics which depend on qualities common to the whole front of the cyclone, viz. a falling barometer, increased warmth and damp, with a muggy, uncomfortable feel of the air, and a dirty sky.

From the increasing damp in this part of a cyclone, while the sky generally is pretty clear, cloud forms round and " caps " the tops of hills, which has given rise to numerous local sayings. The reason is that a hill deflects the air upwards. Usually the cold caused by ascension and consequent expansion is not sufficient to lower the temperature of the air below the dew-point ; but when the air is very damp, the same amount of cooling will bring the air below the dew-point, and so produce condensation.

The gloomy, close, and muggy weather of the front of a cyclone gives rise also to physiological effects in some people ; and animals and birds are sometimes restless.

A glance at the diagram will show that the barometer falls during the whole of the front of the cyclone. Therefore the explanation of the universally known fact that the barometer generally falls for bad weather is, that both rain and wind are usually associated with the front of a cyclone. When we discuss secondaries we shall find a kind of rain for which the barometer does not fall.

Now, to take prognostics which belong to different portions of the cyclone-front, by reference to Fig. 3 it will be seen that in the outskirts of the cyclone-front there is a narrow ring of halo-forming sky. Hence the sayings :—

" Halos predict a storm (rain and wind, or snow and wind) at no great distance, and the open side of the halo tells the quarter from which it may be expected."

" Mock suns predict a more remote and less certain change of weather."

With regard to the open side of the halo indicating the quarter from which the storm may be expected, it does not appear that this can be used as a prognostic with any certainty. It, however, most probably originated in the fact that halos are usually seen in the south-west or west, when the sun or moon is rather low, the lower portion of the halo being cut off by the gloom on the horizon, and that the European storms generally come from those quarters : a heavy bank of cloud will often lie in that direction.

Inside the halo sky comes the denser cloud which gives the pale watery sun and moon. Still nearer the centre we find rain, first in the form of drizzle, then as driving rain. In the left front we find ill-defined showers and a dirty sky.

We have now come to the trough of the cyclone. The line of the trough is often associated with a squall or heavy shower, commonly known as a " clearing shower ". This is much more marked in the portion of the trough which lies to the south of the cyclone's centre than on the northern side.

Then we enter the rear of the cyclone. The whole of the rear is characterized by a cool, dry air, with a brisk, exhilarating feel, and a bright sky, with hard cumulus cloud. These features are the exact converse of those we found in the cyclone-front. In the cloud forms especially we see this difference. All over the front, whether high up or low down, whether as delicate cirrus or heavy gloom, the clouds are of a stratified type. Even under the rain, when we get a peep through a break in the clouds, we find them lying like a more or less thick sheet over the earth. All over the rear, on the contrary, clouds take the rocky form known as cumulus ; cirrus is almost unknown in the rear of a cyclone-centre in the temperate zone.

In the exhilarating quality of the air we find the meaning of the proverb :—

" Do business with men when the wind is in the north-west."

As to the details of the different portions of the rear, immediately behind the centre small patches of blue sky appear. Further from the centre we find showers or cold squalls ; beyond them, hard detached cumulus or stratocumulus ; still farther the sky is blue again.

In the south of the cyclone, near the outskirts the long wispy clouds known as windy cirrus and " mares' tails " are observed. These indicate wind rather than rain, as they are outside of the rainy portion of the cyclone.

So far we have only described the different kinds of weather which would be experienced at the same moment in different places. We have not said much about the sequence of weather at any one place. A single chart tells little about this, for it does not indicate which way the cyclone is going. To track a cyclone we want another chart about twelve or twenty-four hours later, from which we can see exactly how the cyclone centre has moved. Then we can follow the sequence of weather for those twelve or twenty-four hours at any place we choose to select.

It must specially be borne in mind that the word
" front " is a relative term.   In our diagram we have
pointed it to the north-east, because that is the direction
towards which the majority of British cyclones move.
In very rare cases we get a cyclone moving from the south-
east. The general circulation of wind then remains about
the same, but the characteristic qualities of the different
portions of a cyclone are shifted to the new position of the
front and rear. For instance, if the cyclone in our diagram
was moving towards the north-west, we should have muggy
weather and dirty sky with a north-east wind, and bright
weather and clear sky with south-west wind. This occurs
habitually in the northern Tropics, but very rarely in
temperate regions.

But now to take the diagram as it is drawn, we shall
suppose that the centre has moved along the dotted line,
towards the north-east, till it is outside the margin of the
figure. What would the sequence of weather be to an
observer who was living, say, where the word " halo "
is written, just below the word " FRONT " ? This we may
get by taking a line across the diagram, parallel to the
line which marks the track of the cyclone. This will take
us to the word " detached ", just below the word " REAR ".
Following the words and symbols, we should find that
as the barometer began to fall a halo-forming sky would
appear, with the wind coming light from the south-east.
Soon the sky would grow lower and denser, into what
is known as a " watery " sky, and the wind would begin
to veer towards the south and to come in uneasy gusts.
Then drizzling rain would set in, the barometer still
falling, and the muggy, disagreeable feel of the air would
be very noticeable. Later the wind would begin to rise
from the south-west, driving the rain before it, and perhaps
attain the force of a gale. After a time one of the gusts
would be much harder, with heavier rain than any which
had been previously experienced, and with a squall
the wind would go round with a jump two or three points

of the compass to the west or west-north-west. If we looked at the barometer we should find that at that moment the pressure had begun to rise ; this is the passage of the trough of the cyclone. The wind now blows harder than it had done before, and comes in squalls from the north-west, while the whole aspect of the sky and character of weather are changed. The air is cold and dry, the sky is higher and harder, some patches of blue appear in the heavens, hard rocky cumulus appears on the top of the squalls or showers, and the wind moderates. Gradually showers are replaced by masses of cloud from which no rain descends, and after

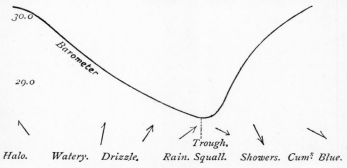

Fig. 4.—Weather sequence in a Cyclone.

a time the sky becomes bright and cloudless, while the wind falls to a gentle breeze.

We have endeavoured to show all this in a diagrammatic form in Fig. 4 ; but observe that, while we read the other diagram from right to left, this one we read in the ordinary manner from left to right. This inversion is obviously necessary, because the paper under the recording pen is moving from right to left. The upper line gives the trace which a self-recording barometer would have marked. In front of the cyclone where the gradients are moderate, the pressure falls slowly ; in rear, where the gradients are steep, it rises rapidly. The arrows below, which are supposed to fly with the wind, mark the shift of the wind which an observer would experience ; and the number of barbs denotes the varying force of the wind. The sequence of weather, which is written in words, is identical with the sequence of weather as marked on the plan of " Prognostics and Weather of a Cyclone ".

Wind is said to " veer " or " haul ", when it changes in the same direction as the course of the sun ; that is, from east, by south, to west, or from west, by north, round to east again. Wind is said, on the contrary, to " back " when it changes against the sun ; that is, from east, by north, to west, and from west, by south, to east again. We have seen that the wind veers to an observer situated to the southward of a cyclone-centre. An inspection of Fig. 3 will show that the wind would back from east to north-east, and then through north to north-west, if the observer were situated anywhere north of the cyclone's path. If he were exactly on the path of the centre, the wind would jump round from south-west to north-east without either veering or backing ; so that by watching the wind anyone can tell what part of a cyclone he is in. In Northern Europe cyclones rarely pass so far to the south as to give the backing sequence. When they do they are almost always soon followed by another cyclone, which passes farther north, and brings fresh bad weather, with another nearly complete shift of wind.

The explanation which we have just given as to the squall which occurs after the barometer has turned in a cyclone, or at the trough of the cyclone, will show the truth of the following :—

> " When rise begins, after low,
> Squalls expect and clear blow."

The clear blow refers to the brighter gale which comes from the north-west, as contrasted with the dirty gale which preceded it from the south-west.

If we take a general view of all the weather in a cyclone

we find that we have a large number of prognostics which precede the rain that is associated with wind and a falling barometer. We shall now refer to a kind of rain which is associated with calm and a stationary barometer.

SECONDARY CYCLONES

A secondary cyclone, or, shortly, a "secondary", is so called both because it has some features in common

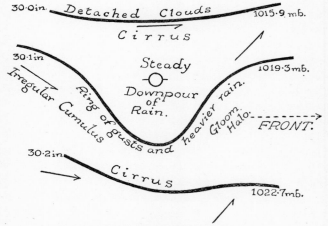

FIG. 5.—Weather in Secondary Cyclone.

with a primary cyclone, and because its origin and motion are frequently determined by the path of the primary. It is, however, often found at the edges of anticyclones. The general appearance of that shape of isobars to which we attach the name of secondary will be readily seen by an inspection of Fig. 5. In that diagram the general slope of the isobars is towards the north, but the isobar of 30·1 inches is bent into a loop, so as to enclose an area of relatively lower pressure, but not a regular pit of low pressure as in a primary cyclone. In consequence of this the isobaric slope is diminished, as the distance between the two adjacent isobars is increased.

For the same reason, the wind inside the loop is very light, but round the edges of the loop the gradient is increased, and the wind is stronger. This wind is usually in angry, violent gusts, and not in the steady, heavy blow of cyclone-wind.

The motion of the secondary is usually parallel to the path of the primary, and it only rarely shows any obvious tendency to revolve round the primary. In fact secondaries generally form on the south side of the primary depression and reach their greatest development there, but they may occasionally form in other parts.

When a secondary is formed at the edge of an anticyclone, the motion is generally very obscure.

Some very striking weather-changes are grouped round this loop of low pressure. In the extreme front we find the thin nebulous cloud which forms halo. Beyond this is a narrow ring of gloomy cirrostratus ; then we find a ring of heavy rain with gusts, surrounding that half of the secondary where the gradients are steepest. Inside this, in the heart of the secondary, we find a calm, with a steady, heavy downpour of rain. On the rear side of the ring of gusts there is a narrow belt of irregular cumulus, beyond which the sky is blue. On the low-pressure side of the secondary we find cirrus and cirrostratus, and outside that the cloud appropriate to the primary cyclone. The general course of the wind follows the universal laws of wind and gradient. The arrows in the diagram show what the direction of the wind would be with the pressure gradients which we have drawn there. We may note that the amount of deflection of the wind is much smaller than in primary cyclones. All over the world secondaries are associated with a peculiar class of thunderstorm.

If the secondary is moving in the direction of the dotted arrow marked " FRONT " on the diagram, the sequence of weather to a single observer would be as

follows. The blue sky would become covered either with
a thin nebulous haze, and perhaps halos, or else with
dirty cirrostratus, and the wind would fall light. The
clouds would rapidly become black and heavy, and soon,
with some angry gusts, heavy rain with big drops would
commence suddenly. We saw before that in a primary
the rain begins as drizzle. If the barometer is very carefully
watched, a very slight rise or fall will be noticed now ;
perhaps only one-hundredth of an inch. This gusty rain
only lasts a few minutes, when the wind falls, and the
rain pours straight down, not quite as heavily as at first.
This stage sometimes lasts four or five hours, and is often
very puzzling to those who are accustomed to associate

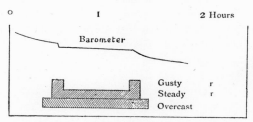

FIG. 6.—Weather Sequence in Secondary.

rain with a falling, and not a steady barometer. When
the rear edge of the secondary approaches, the rain
suddenly becomes much heavier, with more angry gusts.
Just at this moment the barometer moves slightly—
maybe not more than one-hundredth of an inch. If the
general motion of the barometer was upwards when the
rain began, this second motion will be upwards also ;
if downwards, this will be downwards also. Here is another
contrast to a primary cyclone, where a fall of pressure is
always followed by a rise. The heavy rain lasts a very
short time, when the clouds break quickly into irregular
cumulus, and the sky is soon clear again.
    We have endeavoured to show this in the annexed

D

diagram, Fig. 6. The upper curve shows the barometric changes to a single observer. In the secondary of which we have drawn the plan on Fig. 5, the general motion of the barometer would be downwards ; so in Fig. 6 we find that the small motion of the barometer as the secondary approaches is downwards. Then the pressure remains perfectly steady till the disturbance is just going to pass off, when it takes another small step downwards, and then continues to fall slowly, as before the rain began. Below the barogram, the sequence of weather is shown in a diagrammatic form, so as to suggest the ring-like character of the rain. The lowest shaded bar, marked overcast, is drawn under the barogram during the whole time that the sky is overcast. The upper shaded bar is drawn single thickness during the time that the steady downpour is observed, and double thickness under the portions of the barogram during which the heaviest gusty rain is experienced.

We have already alluded to the idea of intensity in any form of atmosphere circulation ; and as simple cloud, moderate, and heavy rain are, as it were, three successive degrees of intensity, the thickness of the bars in the above diagram is proportional to the intensity of the weather in the different portions of a secondary.

There are no special prognostics associated with secondaries. Our object in mentioning the subject here was to explain the nature of another kind of rain than that which is found in primary cyclones. When we come to explain various groups of prognostics, we shall find a number of rain-prognostics which depend on a diminution of barometric pressure. All these indications must obviously be absent before the rain which is produced by a secondary, and we shall now understand why rain often falls without these pressure-prognostics being observed.

ANTICYCLONES

An anticyclone is an area of high pressure. The isobars are normally a considerable distance apart, and extend over a large area. The pressure is highest in the centre, and gradually diminishes outwards. The air is calm and cool in the central portion, while on the outskirts the wind blows round the centre in the direction of the hands of

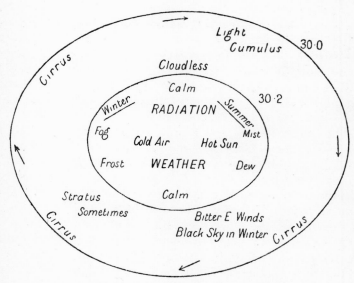

FIG. 7.—Prognostics and Weather of an Anticyclone.

a watch, not exactly parallel to the isobars, but slightly outwards. Unlike a cyclone, which is commonly in rapid motion, an anticyclone is often stationary for many days together.

Thus in Fig. 7 we see that, while there is a dead calm in the centre, the wind comes from the north on the eastern side, from north-east on the south side, from south-east on the western edge, and from west on the northern edge.

The broad features of the weather in an anticyclone are usually, but not always, blue sky, dry cool air, a hot sun, and hazy horizon, with very little wind—in fact, the very antithesis of everything which characterizes a cyclone. As a necessary consequence of this, we find in an anticyclone strongly marked radiation weather, and usually much diurnal variation. These two last ideas are so important that we must devote a few paragraphs to their explanation and consideration.

Radiation weather is best explained by an example. On a very fine summer day we generally find the valleys full of mist in the early morning. As the sun gains power the vapour rises and evaporates, so that the sky becomes cloudless and the sun very hot. After sunset, the air being still and dry, radiation into space from the earth proceeds rapidly, and soon mist forms again in the hollows, and dew upon the grass.

The sequence of a fine day in winter would be similar in general character, but would differ somewhat in details.

Thus, though we have written " fog ", " light cumulus ", " cloudless ", in certain portions of our anticyclone diagram, these words only describe the prominent day-time weather which most affects us in the various portions of the anticyclone ; but the term " RADIATION WEATHER ", written in capital letters, denotes broadly the character by night and by day, in summer or in winter.

Moreover, radiation is only a secondary product of an anticyclone. The primary feature is calm ; radiation effects follow as a matter of course, and the weather due to radiation varies enormously in different latitudes, in different seasons, and in different localities in the same country. In winter surface fog and gloom may predominate.

In a later chapter more will be said about radiation and diurnal variations, but here we may make a few brief remarks.

The theory of radiation is, that when the air is still

the heated surface of the earth radiates into the cold surrounding space, and so the former grows cold enough to condense vapour in the air near the ground, or dew on a suitable surface, such as grass. But when there is more or less wind, each successive layer of air which is in contact with the radiating earth gets removed so rapidly that this condensing process cannot take place, and then no dew or fog is formed. Thus the kind and amount of cloud is variable, but always dependent on radiation.

From the same example of a fine day we can readily pass to the idea of diurnal variation. In the kind of day which we have just described we frequently find a regular sequence from fog to blue, and back again to fog, following the course of the sun—that is, the time of day.

But besides the amount of mist, every other meteorological element has a complex series of changes which depend on the time of day. For instance, both the direction and velocity of the wind have a marked diurnal period, and so has the amount of cloud, the amount of vapour, and every other component of weather. These, and many others, will form the subject of a subsequent chapter. All that we have to note here is the important principle—that the primary character of all weather is given by the shape of the isobars, whether cyclonic, anticyclonic, or otherwise ; that complex diurnal changes are superimposed on this, which modify, but do not alter the intrinsic quality ; and that the resulting weather is the sum of the two together. Thus in a cyclone the changes of weather due to its motion are so marked and so strong that diurnal changes are often entirely obliterated ; while in a calm anticyclone, where there is no motion, the uniform character of the general weather allows full play to radiation, and the diurnal changes are very prominent.

Throughout this work we shall call the character and changes of weather which are due to the shapes of the isobars, the general character and general changes, because they are caused by alterations in the general distribution of pressure over a large portion of the earth's surface. On the contrary, changes which are due to the time of day, the season of the year, or to any local peculiarity, we shall call diurnal, seasonal, or local variations of the general character. The first are really changes, the second only variations. The reason why many prognostics which are due to radiation and diurnal causes are signs of settled weather is because in a country like Britain they can be noticeable only in an anticyclone. An anticyclone means settled weather, not because the weather at any moment in it is fine, but because it is usually stationary, and so there is nothing to change the existing conditions.

We shall now give a few prognostics connected with anticyclones.

The sky being generally clear and the air calm, the temperature is high in the day and low at night. In summer brilliant sunshine prevails during the day, and at night there is a heavy dew, and, in low-lying places, mist.

" Heavy dews in hot weather indicate a continuance of fair weather, and no dew after a hot day foretells rain."

" If mists rise in low ground and soon vanish under the sun, expect fair weather."

Fine, bright, genial weather raises the spirits and exerts an enlivening influence not only on human beings, but also on animals, birds, insects, etc. Hence the sayings :—

" When sea-birds fly out early and far to seaward, moderate winds and fair weather may be expected."

" If rooks go far abroad, it will be fine."

" Cranes soaring aloft and quietly in the air foreshadows fair weather."

" If kites fly high, fine weather is at hand."

" Bats or field-mice coming out of their holes quickly after sunset and sporting themselves in the open air, premonstrates fair and calm weather."

" Chickweed expands its leaves boldly and fully when fine weather is to follow."

These are merely examples of innumerable similar prognostics in all parts of the world.

In winter frost is generally prevalent in the central area of an anticyclone, accompanied frequently by fog, which is most dense in the neighbourhood of large towns. This is all due to the radiation of calm weather.

" White mist in winter indicates frost."

The wind is usually very light in force.

" It is said to be a sign of continued good weather when the wind so changes during the day as to follow the sun."

This " veering with the sun ", as it is called, is the ordinary diurnal variation of the wind, which in Britain is only very obvious with the shallow gradients of an anticyclone. At seaside places in summer very often " the wind is in by day and out by night ", which is the equivalent of the land and sea breezes of the tropics. Like the preceding prognostic, it is only in anticyclones that local currents of air, probably due to unequal heating of sea and land, can override the general circulation of the atmosphere in this country.

Sometimes in winter, on the southern side of the anticyclone, bitter east winds with a black-looking sky will prevail for several days together.

These prognostics apply only so long as the anticyclone remains stationary. Occasionally the anticyclone moves on, and is replaced by some other form of isobars ; but more frequently the anticyclone breaks up—that is to say, it disappears without moving on, and is replaced by a cyclone or some other type of isobars.

WEDGE-SHAPED ISOBARS

We have already defined wedge-shaped isobars as a projecting area of high pressure moving along between two cyclones. This wedge may point in any direction, but in practice by far the most frequently to the north. We have therefore selected such a one for the diagram of the wind and weather in an ideal wedge, which we give in Fig. 8. There the highest pressure is at the bottom of the diagram, while the wedge-shaped isobars project towards the north. On the right hand we see the rear of a retreating cyclone ; on the left, the front of an advancing depression. As these two cyclones move forward,

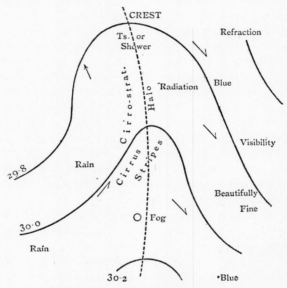

FIG. 8.—Prognostics and Weather of a Wedge.

the wedge goes on between them, so that there must always be a line of stations where, after the barometer has risen owing to the onward passage of the first cyclone, the pressure has just begun to fall, owing to the advance of the second depression. This line is called the crest of the wedge, and is marked by a dotted line in the diagram.

The wind blows round the wedge in accordance with the universal law of gradients. Thus on the east side of

the wedge the wind is from north-west ; in the centre it
is calm ; and on the west side, from south-west to south-
east, as marked by the symbols on the diagram. In
practice the gradients are never steep, so the force of the
wind rarely rises to above that of a pleasant breeze.

The broad features of the cloud and weather in a wedge
are written across the diagram (Fig. 8). In front we find
blue sky, with beautifully fine weather, refraction, and
that unusual clearness of the atmosphere known as
" visibility ". Nearer the calm under the crest we come
to radiation weather, with fog ; and then to halo-bearing
sky just in front of the crest, and stripes of cirrus-cloud.
A thunderstorm or heavy shower is sometimes experienced
at the top of the wedge. In rear of the crest the
sky becomes covered with cirrostratus cloud, and further
in rear we find the rain of the approaching cyclone.

Here, as in cyclones, we see the striking fact that the
words applied to describe the weather contain the
phraseology of many familiar prognostics, such as those
connected with visibility, halos, or the stripes of cirrus
which form the cloud popularly known as " Noah's
Ark ".

If we remember how we took a sort of section across
a cyclone, and so found the sequence of weather at any
station, we shall readily understand that we have only
to read this diagram (Fig. 8) from right to left to get the
sequence of weather during the passage of a wedge.
Thus we should have a beautifully fine day, with a north-
west wind and a rising barometer, with a hot sun by day,
and a cold night with radiation according to the season
of the year. Then, while the barometer was still rising,
the blue sky would assume that peculiar nebulous white-
ness which forms halos, and stripes of cirrus would appear
in places. Soon the barometer would begin to fall, the
sky to grow denser and overcast, and before long the
drizzling rain of the new cyclone would begin to fall,
the wind having previously backed to the south-west.

We now see the meaning of the halo and the cirrus-stripes being marked in the diagram partly in front of the crest of the wedge, viz. that in a wedge the sky shows the approach of a new cyclone before the barometer at a single station has ceased to rise. This is very interesting, as it is the first opportunity we have had of explaining why the barometer sometimes appears to fail, and rises, as in this case, while bad weather is manifestly approaching. It also shows the great additional power of forecasting which the use of synoptic charts gives to a meteorologist, in a central office, with abundant telegraphic communication. Suppose any morning that a forecaster found that his isobars were wedge-shaped. He could then indicate to the eastern districts of his territory that the fine weather would not last, though they with their rising barometer might have thought the contrary.

It may be remarked here that all cyclones are not preceded by a wedge, but only those which roll, as it were, along the northern edge of a large stationary anticyclone.

We can now explain the prognostics that are marked on the diagram, and several others for which there was no room. Any appearance of the sky which characterizes the front of a wedge will be a sign of rain, because there is always rain in rear of that shape of isobars. These prognostics of wet which are associated with fine, dry weather are particularly interesting, because they are the very opposite of the rain-prognostics in a cyclone, which are associated with increasing damp and a dirty sky.

It used to be thought that every prognostic of rain would be explained by showing that the appearance was due to an increase of vapour in the air ; here we find that the prognostic could only be explained on the supposition that many cyclones develop an area of calm and clear sky in front of, and as a portion of, themselves. It is a crude idea of meteorology to think . that all rain-prevision depends on hygrometry.

Returning now to Fig. 8, we see that in the rear of the retreating cyclone the air is dry and the weather beautifully fine—of the sort of which we should say it was " too fine to last ".

During the day the sun is burning hot.

" When the sun burns more than usual, rain may be expected."

During the night white frost is formed, owing to calm radiation.

" A white frost never lasts more than three days ; a long frost is a black frost."

" Frost suddenly following heavy rain, seldom lasts long."

As the day advances, after a white frost, the air becomes dull from the influence of the oncoming depression. Whence the saying :—

" When the frost gets into the air, it will rain."

During the very fine weather on the east side of a wedge-shaped area there is often great visibility, with a cloudless sky.

" The further the sight, the nearer the rain."

This is one kind of visibility ; there is another class that is associated with a hard, overcast sky, as we shall explain under " straight isobars ".

At the extreme north-west edge of a cyclone there is often a particular kind of " refraction "—a well-known sign of rain. This seems to be due to the cold air in the rear of a cyclone being much below the temperature of the sea. If so it is a sign of rain for the reason that one cyclone is usually soon followed by another. There is another kind of refraction caused by a cool south-east wind in an anticyclone blowing over a heated sea, which is usually a sign of fine weather. This is a good illustration of how the same prognostic may portend either good or bad weather, according to its surroundings, and of the limitations generally of prognostics unsupported by synoptic information.

If the cyclone in front of the wedge has produced
a north-west gale, it is not improbable that the oncoming
one may begin with a south-west gale.   Hence the
significance of the well-known nautical saying on the
Atlantic :—

" A nor'-wester is not long in debt to a sou'-wester."

In the cyclone and secondary we have found rain of
different kinds ; so in the anticyclone and wedge we have
found fine weather of different kinds.   Anticyclone fine
weather is almost always hazy, and is settled weather,
because the anticyclone itself is usually stationary.
Wedge fine weather is always clear, and is only temporary
because the wedge is never stationary.   Hence we see
that when we talk of rain and fine weather, it is often
necessary to say what kind of rain and what kind of fine
weather ; and we find, moreover, that a knowledge of the
kind of isobars enables us to define the kind of weather.
In purely statistical discussions on climate and
meteorology much confusion may be caused by lack of
classification.

The prognostics which are associated with a wedge
are almost less liable to failure than those which accompany other shapes of isobars.   When they do fail, it is
usually from a sudden break-up of all the existing
distribution of pressure.

STRAIGHT ISOBARS

Straight isobars are so called because the isobars have
no curvature.   The trend of the lines may be in any
direction, and so may their slope.   For instance, the lines
may lie east and west, but the slope may be either towards
the north or towards the south.   In our general diagram
(Fig. 2) of all the fundamental shapes of isobars, we drew
some straight isobars sloping to the south.   In temperate
regions this slope is uncommon, while a slope to the
north or north-west is very common.   We have therefore

selected an instance of a northerly slope for our diagram of straight isobars in Fig. 9, and, as before, have written in words the kind of sky and weather which we find in different parts of the slope. In all other shapes of isobars which we have hitherto described, the lines enclose an area of high or low pressure, while in straight isobars the lines only mark the position of what may be called a barometric slope.

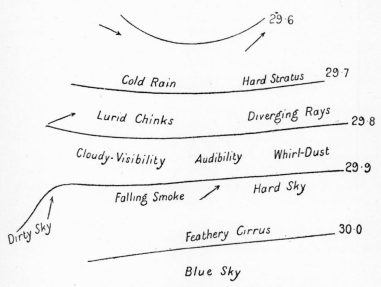

FIG. 9.—Prognostics and Weather in Straight Isobars.

On turning to Fig. 9 it will be seen that while the pressure is high to the south, it is generally low to the north, without any definite cyclonic system, and that the isobars run straight nearly east and west, with a slope towards the north. The wind is from the south-west or west, and usually strong and gusty, but short of a gale. On the high-pressure side the sky is blue ; then as we approach the low-pressure, feathery cirrus, or some form of windy sky, makes it appearance, while a blustery wind whirls the dust up or blows the smoke down.

Getting still nearer the low-pressure, the sky is found to be gathering into hard stratocumulus, at first with chinks between its masses, through which divergent rays stream down under the sun, which is spoken of as "the sun drawing water". Sometimes, especially in winter, these rays are lurid, and the appearance of the sky is then very striking. This prognostic is common all over Northern Europe, and in Denmark takes the form of "Locke is drawing water". Loki is a well-known demi-god in the Scandinavian Eddas, so that we have here a direct survival of mythic speech. This hard stratocumulus is especially characteristic of straight isobars in Great Britain.

At the same time there is often great "visibility", with a hard, overcast sky and moderately dry air, in which the cloud seems to play the part of a sunshade, for as soon as the sun comes out the clearness of distant objects diminishes. This visibility must not be confounded with the visibility already described with a cloudless sky, which occurs with wedge-shaped isobars.

Simultaneously we often find "audibility". This distinctness of distant sounds must be distinguished from the case where sounds which are not usually heard, are brought up by the wind coming from a favourable quarter. For instance, the whistle of a railway-train to the south of a house may not be usually heard with the normal south-west wind of Great Britain ; but when the wind backs to the south in front of a depression, then the noise will be heard ; and though this will be a good prognostic, still, it is not true audibility.

When the gradients are very steep a little rain sometimes falls with straight isobars, generally in light showers, with a hard sky.

Though, as a matter of convenience, we have described the sequence of weather as we proceed from the high to the low pressure, it must be clearly understood that it does not represent the sequence of weather to a single observer, but rather what the weather will be simultaneously in different parts of the country ; for instance, that if there is cirrus in London, there may perhaps be a lurid sky in Edinburgh.

But now audibility, visibility, whirling dust, and lurid chinks with divergent rays are well-known signs of rain almost all over the world, so we have to explain why the appearance of the sky in straight isobars is a sign of rain. It is found by experience that straight isobars are never persistent, and that, practically, the district which they cover one day will be traversed by a cyclone the next day. It does not follow that the cyclone is necessarily in existence when we observe the straight isobars ; but from the nature of weather changes, straight isobars seem to be an intermediate and unstable form of atmospheric circulation which precedes the formation of a cyclone.

We cannot, therefore, draw a section across straight isobars and say that it will give the sequence of weather at any place, for we are not dealing with a moving form of pressure, but with a transitional state of things which cannot last long. The chief interest of these rain prognostics lies in the contrast which they present to those associated with a cyclone. While those in a cyclone are accompanied by an almost ominous calm and a dirty, murky sky, these are associated with a hard sky and blustery wind, of which it would be ordinarily remarked " that the wind keeps down the rain ", or " that when the wind falls, it will rain ". While, also, the prognostics which precede cyclone-rain hold good for the reason that they are seen in front of the rainy portion of such a depression, those associated with straight isobars hold good because, though there is little rain actually with them, the area which they cover to-day will probably be covered by a cyclone to-morrow—the conditions being favourable for the passage of depressions. Another point of contrast lies in the comparative dryness of the air in straight isobars, as compared with the excessive amount of moisture which preceded cyclones. The same remarks apply to these as to the fine-weather prognostics associated with wedge-shaped isobars.

All the prognostics we have discussed under this heading fail when the straight isobars are formed during a general rearrangement of the whole distribution of pressure over the northern hemisphere, because a cyclone may not then traverse the district where the well-known signs of rain had been observed.

GENERAL REMARKS

The details which we have given abundantly show that every portion of every shape of isobars has a characteristic weather and look of sky, and that prognostics simply describe these appearances.

Theoretically, then, when the isobars are well defined, we ought to be able to write down the prognostics which might be visible everywhere, but practically we cannot do so completely ; and also, theoretically, all that any prognostic does is perhaps to enable a solitary observer to identify his position in any kind of atmospheric circulation. Thus the associates of the front of a cyclone or secondary are signs of bad weather ; while those of the rear of a cyclone, or of any portion of an anticyclone, are signs of fine weather. The word " front " implies not only the idea of motion, but also of the direction of that motion. But here comes in the reason why prognostics can never develop the science of forecasting much further than at present. Depressions have a way of advancing so far in a certain direction, and then of either changing their front or else dying out altogether. Probably no prognostic can give any clue to the probability of either of these changes. On the other hand, a forecaster with synoptic charts can often tell when a cyclone is going to be arrested or deflected from its previous course, and this branch of the science is still capable of extension.

In the first chapter we mentioned the peculiarity that all rain-prognostics are not associated with increasing or excessive damp. The reason for this is that there are different kinds of rain, such as the rain in front of a primary cyclone, which is associated with great damp ; and the light showers of straight isobars, which are associated with a rather dry air. Also, that some rain-prognostics, such as those associated with the much too fine weather in front of a wedge, owe their value to the fact that a wedge precedes a cyclone, though the air in itself is tolerably dry.

A similar train of argument applies to the question why rain and fine weather are not always preceded by the same prognostics. We have just mentioned two different sorts of rain, and, as regards fine weather, we need only mention that in a like manner there are many kinds of fine weather. For instance, the formation of small blue patches in an otherwise overcast sky in rear of a cyclone foretells one kind of fine weather, while the radiation phenomena of an anticyclone also indicate fine weather, but of a totally different sort.

We have shown why the value of the indications which prognostics afford can never be materially improved, but at the same time perhaps no advance in synoptic meteorology will ever supersede entirely the use of prognostics. For example in the tropics, as in Europe, unusual coloration of the sky at sunrise and sunset apparently often precedes the formation of any notable barometric depression ; so that sometimes the indications of prognostics are ahead of those of any other system of forecasting. In isolated stations, and on board ship especially, an observer must often rely to a great extent on his own eyes to gather information from the aspect of the sky as well as from the readings of his own barometer.

E

We shall not in this work make any further specific reference to the problem of how much weather-forecasting a solitary observer, without telegraphic reports, can do for himself ; but in later chapters it will become evident that there are many cases where purely local observation of sky, wind, and barometric changes can assist the solitary observer in drawing inferences as to the probable synoptic situation and therefore as to the probable sequence of weather.

Chapter III

THE UPPER AIR

Methods of Observation

In the systematic exploration which has taken place since near the end of last century, various methods have been employed for obtaining information about the atmosphere at high levels. At a much earlier period observations made on mountains and from manned balloons had revealed the general nature of the variation of temperature up to moderate elevations. With small unmanned balloons, however, very much greater heights can be reached, 15 to 20 km. quite commonly, and even greater heights on occasions. These ballons sondes, as they are called, carry meteorographs, that is, self-registering instruments, arranged as a rule to record pressure and temperature and sometimes also humidity. The highly ingenious British type of meteorograph, designed by the late W. H. Dines, weighs, complete, only 2 oz. The actual record is scratched on a thin silver-plated piece of metal about the size of a postage stamp. The balloons themselves are made of thin rubber, and are inflated with hydrogen to a diameter, at the start, of some 5 or 6 feet. When one of these balloons is set free it rises in the atmosphere at a rate of nearly 1,000 feet a minute, and it continually expands, owing to the diminishing pressure around it ; this expansion enables it to retain its buoyancy and keep on rising to very great heights. Ultimately the balloon either bursts or begins to leak, and comes down again, the parachute-action of the balloon serving to break the force of the fall. A label attached to the instruments invites the finder to detach the instrument and return it to a central observatory.

The record engraved on the silvered plate is read by means of a microscope of special design. Essentially the record is a graph of temperature against pressure. The first step in interpreting the results is to tabulate the pressure and temperature for a number of selected points on the record. We have already explained that pressure at any level is simply weight of atmosphere above that level. Thus the difference of pressure between any two levels is a measure of the mass of atmosphere between these two levels. Knowing the pressure and knowing the temperature we can compute the density of the air and in turn the thickness of this mass of atmosphere. The formula giving the height of the air column between two levels is—

$$h = 18400 \ \frac{T}{273} \ (log_{10}p_0 - log_{10}p)$$

where T is the mean temperature of the air column in $°A$, h the height of the air column in metres, p_0 and p the pressure at the bottom and top of the column.

In this way starting from the point which relates to ground level we can compute, step by step, the heights corresponding to the various points on the record of pressure and temperature.

It may be mentioned incidentally that an altimeter is in effect simply an aneroid barometer with its scale graduated for height by means of the above formula, instead of directly in pressure units.

Lower levels of the atmosphere can be explored readily by means of kites or aeroplanes.

Measurement of upper winds is carried out more simply by means of small balloons known as pilot balloons, the drift of which, as they rise into the air, can be watched by observers equipped with a special type of theodolite.

Information about the air at much greater heights has been obtained indirectly by other ingenious methods. One of these depends on the manner in which sound waves are propagated. On occasions when great explosions occur or heavy guns are fired it is found that within the radius of extreme audibility [1] there lies in general a "zone of silence"; the outer region of audibility lying beyond this zone of silence begins at a distance of about 100 miles from the source of sound and may extend to 150 miles or more. The only feasible explanation of this outer zone of audibility is that the sound rays going out into the upper atmosphere become curved down again on reaching a certain level; that in turn means that the rays at this high level travel even faster than they do at ground level and this in turn requires either a change in constitution of the atmosphere at the level in question or a rise in temperature. For reasons into which it is not possible to enter here the latter is considered the more probable. Calculation suggests that the level at which the sound rays recurve is about 40 km. above the earth, and that the temperature when that height is reached has risen again to roughly the same as at the earth's surface; also that at a level of 55 km. the temperature may have risen as high as $170°$ F.

That a high temperature exists at or above this level was first suggested by computations based on observations relating to the appearance of meteors.

There are other indirect ways in which our knowledge of the atmosphere is now being extended to greater levels, namely, in the study of terrestrial magnetism, of the aurora, and of the propagation of wireless waves.

By far the greater part of all our information, however, relates to the first 20 or 30 km., and the meteorological importance of anything beyond these levels will not concern us in this work.

GENERALIZATIONS

The information obtained by these various methods has led to important conclusions. Stated in the most general

---

[1] The "audibility" to which reference is made on p. 46 relates to hearing of sounds at distances of a few miles. It is governed by the structure of the lowest layers of air.

way, the atmosphere surrounding the earth may be regarded as consisting of two shells. In the lower, known as the troposphere, which varies in thickness from some 8 km. in arctic regions to some 16 km. in the tropics, temperature falls usually at a more or less regular rate of about 1° F per 100 metres. At the surface and all levels up to 8 km. the air is much warmer at the Equator than at the poles, but as the rate of fall in equatorial regions is maintained for about another 8 km., the result is to make the final temperature over the Equator at a height of 16 km. lower than the temperature over the poles at a height of 8 km. The upper surface of the troposphere is known as the tropopause, from the circumstance that the fall of temperature characteristic of the troposphere pauses here.

In the upper shell of atmosphere, known as the stratosphere, temperature does not appear to vary appreciably with height but is approximately constant until a height of some 30 to 40 km. above the earth has been reached. The temperature in this isothermal region, as it is sometimes though not quite accurately called, ranges from about − 60° F over the Arctic Circle to about − 100° F over the tropical regions. Above a height of 40 km. the temperature, as has already been stated, rises again very greatly, to perhaps 170° F at a height of 55 km., it is supposed. The high temperature at these levels was at first attributed to the presence of ozone which absorbs nearly all the ultra-violet rays from sunlight and absorbs also some heat rays at the lower end of the spectrum. Quite recently, however, evidence has been forthcoming which suggests that most of the ozone in the atmosphere lies between the heights of 15 and 20 km., so that some other explanation may have to be found for the high temperature at a height of 55 km.

In the study of weather we are concerned almost entirely with the troposphere, the region in which storms occur and in which float all but the most ethereal clouds, and very much are we concerned with the temperature and humidity at various heights in this region.

PHYSICAL PROCESSES

The rate at which temperature varies with height is known as the lapse rate and its average value in the troposphere, as we have said, is a fall of 1° F per 100 metres, or, roughly, 3° F per 1,000 feet. The reader will naturally ask why the air in the troposphere should be arranged in this manner in regard to temperature and not have, for example, the same temperature at all heights, as happens in the lower part of the stratosphere. At the end of this chapter we shall go into the reasons, so far as they have been developed at the present time, for the different arrangements of temperature in the stratosphere and troposphere. As to the latter, however, we may say at once here that the principal cause of decrease of temperature with height is turbulence or mixing and this process will now be discussed.

The lower layers of air in various ways are partially stirred up so that sometimes masses of air from one level are raised to change places with masses of air at another level. Now an important means of cooling air is by raising it to a greater height and a corresponding means of warming is to lower it to a less height. The reason for this cooling or warming with change of height is as follows :—

Any mass of air which is raised to higher levels is subjected thereby to less and less barometric pressure and therefore it expands ; and further, it is a physical fact that air which expands adiabatically—that is, without any heat being communicated to it during the process—becomes colder. The latter fact may be demonstrated quite simply by releasing air which has been kept under pressure—for example, in the tube of a pneumatic tyre. This process is known as dynamical cooling. Conversely air may be dynamically warmed by compressing it—a simple demonstration being the pumping up of a pneumatic tyre. Wherever a mass of air rises to regions of lower pressure it is dynamically cooled in this way, the fall of temperature being at the rate of 5·4° F for every 1,000 feet of rise so long as no water vapour is actually condensed. This is known technically as the dry adiabatic lapse rate. It is frequently found in the lower layers of air on sunny days over land surfaces, but under average conditions the fall of temperature with height is not so fast as this, being, as we have remarked, usually only about 3° F per 1000 feet, and that is partly because the presence of moisture introduces a complication.

All air in nature is more or less moist. The moisture initially comes from the ocean and other water or moist surfaces, evaporation taking place from these surfaces when they are warmed by the sun's rays. The amount of moisture that air can contain in the form of invisible vapour depends on the temperature—the higher the temperature, the more water vapour may be present. When there is the maximum amount possible for the temperature, the air is said to be saturated. It is customary to express the actual amount of water vapour present as a percentage of the maximum amount which could be contained at the given temperature, and this percentage is known as the relative humidity, a condition of saturation being, of course, expressed by a relative humidity of 100 per cent.

If any air be cooled sufficiently a point will sooner or later be reached (known as the dew-point) when the air is saturated, and then water vapour will be condensed out and will appear in the form of cloud or water drops. Such cooling may sometimes, for example, take place at night and cause dew or some mist or ground fog. But a more important manner of cooling is that just described, namely, by the ascent of air to great heights.

If the air continues to rise after water vapour begins to condense the temperature will continue to fall and cloud eventually will form, but the rate of fall of temperature will then be considerably less rapid than the dry adiabatic rate, in fact only about 3° F per 1,000 feet, and this is known as the saturated adiabatic lapse rate. There is a reason for the less rapid fall. A considerable amount of heat is required in the first instance to evaporate water and convert it into invisible vapour ; the same amount of heat is given up whenever vapour condenses back to the liquid form ; the air in which the condensation takes place shares in this " latent " heat as it becomes available, and thus the air as it rises to greater heights falls less rapidly in temperature than would be the case if no condensation were taking place.

STABILITY AND INSTABILITY

In discussing the question of the stability or instability of arrangement of the atmosphere it is customary to imagine a mass of air as isolated from the atmosphere as a whole, and to consider what degree of buoyancy the mass has in relation to its " surroundings " or " environment " ; but it must be kept in mind that it is really the condition of things in the " surroundings " that we wish to elucidate.

Various causes may lead to the ascent of air and in some cases to the formation of visible cloud. Any mass of air that becomes more heated and therefore less dense than its surroundings will rise and must continue to rise so long as it is warmer than its environment. Now if the lapse rate in the environment is equivalent to the dry adiabatic rate, and if a small mass of air be made ever so slightly warmer than the other air at its original level, we see that this small mass will go on rising indefinitely, because it will continue to be warmer at every level than the other air at the same level. If, however, the environment has some slightly less lapse rate than the dry adiabatic one then the small mass in question will soon reach a level at which its temperature becomes the same as that of the environment, and then it will be in equilibrium with the surrounding air and will have no further buoyancy, always assuming that the rising mass is sufficiently dry for no condensation to take place during this process.

We see, therefore, that the smaller the lapse rate in the atmosphere as a whole the more will the conditions tend to check vertical movements of masses of air. For a moderate degree of stability to exist even in fairly dry air the actual lapse rate requires to be markedly less than the dry adiabatic lapse rate. In such a case the different layers of atmosphere tend to preserve their existing stratification. Sir Napier Shaw has given to this quality the name " resilience " (or " springiness "), defining it as " the distribution of forces in a continuous material which is called into play when the material is deformed, and which causes the material to return to its original shape if the deforming forces are gradually removed, or which sets up oscillations about the original configuration if the disturbing forces suddenly cease to act ".

Stability clearly is increased if the air is relatively dry. On the other hand, if an air mass which we are considering is nearly saturated a very small upward movement will produce condensation and thereafter the decrease of temperature resulting from any further upward movement will be at the relatively slow saturated adiabatic rate. Thus unless the lapse rate in the environment is very small indeed the moist rising mass will have a very good chance of retaining some buoyancy relative to its surroundings and will tend to go on rising ; in other words, an atmosphere heavily charged with moisture, especially in its lower layers, is one that, other things being equal, tends to lack resiliency, to be unstable in its vertical arrangement, and to be liable to permanent deformation when subjected to local or unequal heating or increase of moisture content.

In some countries observations of temperature and humidity in the upper air up to heights of some 20,000 feet are now obtained daily by the use of aeroplanes, so that precise and detailed information as to the thermal structure of the atmosphere is generally available. These observations are of practical utility in weather forecasting ; and in the Upper Air Supplement to the Daily Weather Report issued by the British Meteorological Office they are plotted on charts of which Fig. 10 is a specimen.

It will be noted that the framework of the diagram consists
of horizontal and vertical lines which are not quite equally
spaced, successive pairs being gradually more widely spaced
as one proceeds from bottom to top and from right to left.
Actually the scales are logarithmic scales, and the reason

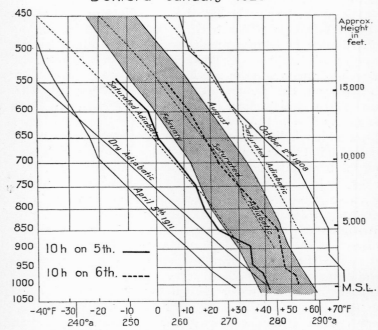

UPPER AIR TEMPERATURES

Duxford   January   1928

FIG. 10.—Upper Air Temperatures on 5th and 6th January, 1928.

for choosing logarithmic rather than linear scales is one of
convenience. When pressure and temperature are plotted
on these scales all changes of temperature according to the
dry adiabatic rate are represented by straight lines, whilst
heights can be represented approximately linearly.

The background of the diagram contains details against

which any particular set of observations is intended to be compared. The shaded belt running across the diagram is bounded on the right by the line indicating the mean run of the temperature in August and on the left by the line indicating the mean run in February. These two lines are derived from the averages of many series of observations in what are usually the warmest and coldest months respectively.

The most steeply sloping of all the lines of reference is that labelled Dry Adiabatic. As we have seen, any distribution of temperature which shows as steep a lapse rate as this line is a very unstable case indeed. There is no need to draw more than one Dry Adiabatic on the diagram because on the framework adopted the Dry Adiabatic becomes a straight line, i.e. it has a constant slope at all heights. The Saturated Adiabatics, however, that is the lines which indicate how a mass of saturated air would decrease in temperature as it rose in the atmosphere, depend on the temperature of the air when it starts rising and their slope is less according as the temperature (and thus the possible water content of the air) is higher. Thus for convenience three of these Saturated Adiabatics are drawn. It will be noticed that the one representing the coldest mass of air has the steepest slope and, indeed, that by the time it reaches the greatest height allowed for on the diagram it is sloping nearly as steeply as the Dry Adiabatic ; this is simply because its actual water content has then become so low as not to make much difference. If these Saturated Adiabatics are examined more closely it will be seen that the last mentioned begins at a temperature of freezing point (32° F) and that the other two, when they come to this temperature, cease for a short distance to fall any further in regard to temperature, i.e. the saturated masses of air which they represent rise at this stage for a short step in height without undergoing any decrease of temperature. Apparently these air masses have received some small accession of heat and the reason for this is once again a question of " latent heat ".

In this case the " latent heat " is that given up when the water that is being condensed all the way up is at this stage quickly changed from the liquid state to the solid state, i.e. to ice or snow.

Finally on the diagram there are two outer reference lines, labelled respectively 2nd October, 1908, and 5th April, 1911. These are in the nature of " records "—being respectively the warmest and the coldest upper air ascents made in the British Isles during a considerable period of years.

The object of all these reference lines is to present a background against which the special features of any particular ascent may be readily estimated. We can see at a glance not only their relation to the average conditions for the season of the year, but also the degree of stability or instability of the atmospheric stratification at any particular level.

On the diagram we have plotted the temperature observations of two ascents made at Duxford in January, 1928. One relates to 10 a.m. on 5th, the other to 10 a.m. on 6th ; something more is said about them in Chapter V.

INVERSIONS

We occasionally find cases where there is an actual inversion of the lapse rate, i.e. where the temperature— generally over quite a small range of height—actually increases with height, or at least does not diminish. Such cases are known briefly as " inversions ". There is generally an inversion at the top of a layer of fog and, indeed, of other clouds of stratified type. In fact the air under inversions is frequently moist while the air just above them is usually very dry. It will be realized that a strong inversion greatly improves the degree of stability of the atmosphere and forms a very effective barrier to any rising parcel of air, or to any turbulence or convection from beneath. On this account the term " convective lid " has been very appropriately applied to inversions. The tropopause is an example of an inversion.

We return to questions of stability and instability and give some applications in the chapters on Diurnal Variation and on Line Squalls respectively.

THE ATMOSPHERE ABOVE CYCLONES AND ANTICYCLONES

The height of the tropopause in temperate latitudes varies at different times and shows a fairly definite relationship with the distribution of barometric pressure at ground level, being sometimes as high as 12 km. in areas of high pressure and as low as 8 or 9 km. in areas of low pressure.

We give below a table, compiled from observations by W. H. Dines, showing the average values of pressure and temperature at different levels over high and low pressure areas respectively.

TABLE II
PRESSURE AND TEMPERATURE OVER HIGH AND LOW PRESSURE AREAS

Height	Pressure over		Temperature over		Differences between "High" and "Low"	
	"Low"	"High"	"Low"	"High"	Pressure	Temperature
km.	mb.	mb.	°A	°A	mb.	°A
14	135	146	224	215	11	− 9
13	157	171	226	215	14	− 11
12	183	201	225	217	18	− 8
11	212	235	225	221	22	− 4
10	247	273	225	226	26	1
9	288	317	226	233	29	7
8	335	366	227	240	31	13
7	388	422	232	247	34	15
6	449	483	240	254	34	14
5	516	552	248	261	36	13
4	591	628	255	267	37	12
3	675	713	263	272	38	9
2	767	807	269	277	40	8
1	870	913	275	279	43	4
0	984	1031	279	282	47	3

It will be seen here that in the case of the low pressure area temperature practically ceases to fall above a height of 8 km., whilst in the case of the high pressure the fall is maintained until about the 12 km. level.

The second last column gives the difference of pressure between " high " and " low " at various heights and contains a second point of interest, namely, that until a height of about 9 km. has been reached, there is no very rapid diminution in this difference.

The last column gives the difference of temperature between " high " and " low " at various heights and indicates a very important distinction between high and low pressure conditions, namely that, at least above a height of 1 or 2 kilometres, the troposphere on the average at any fixed level is very definitely warmer in anticyclonic conditions than in cyclonic conditions, whilst the stratosphere at any fixed level is colder in anticyclonic conditions than in cyclonic conditions.

It will be seen that the features of the upper air over the anticyclone resemble in a general way those of the upper air over tropical regions, whilst the features of the upper air over cyclones resemble those found over polar regions.

As a possible explanation of the remarkable distribution of temperature in the upper air over cyclones and anti-cyclones, W. H. Dines has suggested the action of some force acting nearly horizontally at about the level of the tropopause and directed outward from the cyclone towards the anticyclone. In the cyclone we can imagine this force as drawing up the air of the troposphere and drawing down the air of the stratosphere ; and it can be shown that the result of these operations would be to render the upward drawn air of the troposphere at each level rather colder than the normal for that level, and the downward drawn air of the stratosphere rather warmer at each level than the normal for that level.

In the anticyclone we imagine the force as pressing down

the air of the troposphere and pressing up the air of the
stratosphere, with results opposite to those just described.

RADIATION

Extremely small amounts of heat come from the interior
of the earth, from chemical action and other minor sources,
but one may say that the principal source of all heat in
the atmosphere is radiation from the sun. The amount
received at any given place on the earth's surface varies
according to the latitude of the place and the season of
the year. The nature and extent of these variations is
indicated in a table in Chapter VIII.

Exact observation in recent years has shown also that
the amount of radiation emitted by the sun is not absolutely
constant ; in other words, the sun is a variable star, but
the variations in radiation observed so far do not amount
to more than a few per cent, and it cannot be said that any
clear relation has yet been found between the weather
experienced and the changes in what is known as the " solar
constant ". In any case the details of such changes or the
seasonal or latitude variations will not concern us further
for the present (they will be mentioned again in a later
chapter), but only the broad results when the solar radiation,
supposed of sensibly constant intensity, reaches the
earth's atmosphere.

It is necessary to explain in the first place that the sun's
radiation comprises a wide range of wave lengths, the
short ultra-violet rays which produce chemical effects, the
light rays of the visible part of the spectrum violet to red,
and the long heat or infra-red rays. It happens that the
two gases, oxygen and nitrogen, which constitute by far
the greater part of the atmosphere, allow nearly all these
solar rays and also long-wave radiation such as that given
out by the earth itself, to pass quite freely through them,
and absorb very little of the energy of these rays. Thus if
the earth's atmosphere consisted solely of oxygen and

nitrogen the surface of the earth would be raised to a rather
high temperature during the day, and would cool to a very
low temperature every night. Water vapour, however,
is always present in the atmosphere, and it absorbs some of
the solar rays in the visible part of the spectrum and is
an important absorbent of much of the heat rays. Also,
a large part of the long-wave radiation from the ground is
absorbed by water vapour. Thus the absorbing power of
water vapour plays a very important part in determining
how warm the air becomes and how much the sun's rays
are tempered by the time they reach the ground. Moreover,
when clouds are present in the atmosphere they reflect a good
deal of the radiation ; and it has been estimated that the
light reflected from clouds, from the sea, and from the air
accounts in all for about half of the radiation arriving from
the sun ; the other half remains to be absorbed by the
earth, and eventually radiated out again as long-wave
radiation. Dr. G. C. Simpson has pointed out that cloud
acts like a thermostat in controlling the temperature of the
lower atmosphere, in that an increase in the sun's radiation
would lead to more cloud which in turn would increase the
proportion of light and heat reflected away from the earth.
It is interesting in this connection to note that the planet
Venus which is nearer to the sun than is the earth, and
therefore exposed to much more intense radiation, is completely covered in clouds, whilst Mars, which is farther
away, is quite clear of cloud.

Other gases present in the atmosphere in very small
quantities, namely, carbon dioxide and ozone, are important
absorbents of certain kinds of radiation. The latter has
already been mentioned in connection with the high
temperature of the air, which is believed to occur at heights
of 40 to 60 km.

What has been said so far in this section relates largely
to information derived from facts which can be demonstrated by laboratory experiments. The problem of the
part played by radiation in the atmosphere, however, is

F

an extremely complex one and many of its aspects are still far from clear. Any given layer of the atmosphere must be regarded as radiating heat in all directions and at the same time as receiving from other sources a certain amount of radiation, part of which is absorbed and part transmitted.

The final temperature of the layer would be determined by the balance between the radiation absorbed and that emitted, if it were not for the complication of convection, which, as we have seen in an earlier part of this chapter, begins to operate, causing vertical exchange of air, as soon as the rate of fall of temperature in the vertical direction exceeds the adiabatic rate.

In an earlier part also we have described the two shells of the atmosphere known as the troposphere and stratosphere, in the first of which temperature falls at a fairly regular rate and in the second of which temperature varies little with height. The application of what is known about radiation and convection to the problem of explaining why the atmosphere should be so arranged has been worked out by Col. E. Gold. He calculates that above a certain height, which depends on the water content of the atmosphere and approximates closely to the height of the tropopause, the distribution of temperature is controlled largely by the processes of radiation whilst convection has little opportunity to occur. Below this height, however, radiation normally works in such a way that any layer of the atmosphere tends to lose more heat by radiation than it absorbs, whilst all the time the total radiation coming downward through the layer exceeds that going outward. In these conditions the layer in question would keep on getting cooler relatively to the layers below it, so that sooner or later the lapse rate of temperature would reach the adiabatic rate; then convection would start in an attempt to restore equilibrium and so the process would go on indefinitely. Thus below the critical height calculated by Gold, the distribution of temperature would be determined ultimately and mainly by the convectional process and this as we have seen means a more or less regular fall of temperature with height.

The strong insolation and the high air temperatures at lower levels in tropical regions cause the air there to have a high content of water vapour as compared with the air in temperate latitudes or in polar regions. It will thus be seen that the line of reasoning set out above, to explain the existence of troposphere and stratosphere, can be further employed to explain the greater height of the tropopause in tropical as compared with polar latitudes. At the same time it has to be recognized that these problems are still far from being completely and satisfactorily solved.

BIBLIOGRAPHY

The Characteristics of the Free Atmosphere. W. H. Dines. London: Meteorological Office Geoph. Mem., No. 13. Price 2s.

The International Kite and Balloon Ascents. E. Gold. London: Meteorological Office Geoph. Mem., No. 5.

Manual of Meteorology, vol. iii. Sir Napier Shaw. Camb. Univ. Press.

The Temperature of the Atmosphere at Levels Accessible to Air Waves. F. J. W. Whipple. Terr. Magn. and At. Elecy., vol. 38, pp. 13–16 (1933).

Further Studies in Terrestrial Radiation. G. C. Simpson. Roy. Met. Soc. Mem., vol. iii, No. 21.

CHAPTER IV

CLOUDS

NOMENCLATURE

IN approaching the subject of cloud types it is desirable to direct attention first to the four terms, introduced by Luke Howard, on which the nomenclature of the various forms is built up.

1. *Cirrus.*—All cloud which has a fibrous, feathery or curly look is given the name cirrus or has the word cirro in combination.

2. *Cumulus.*—All cloud which has a rocky or lumpy look is either cumulus or has the word cumulo in combination.

3. *Stratus.*—All cloud which lies as a thin flat sheet is either stratus or has the word strato in combination.

4. *Nimbus.*—With an exception to be noted later, any cloud from which rain is falling is nimbus in some form.

In 1930 the International Commission for the Study of Clouds adopted the following simple classification of the chief types, according to the heights at which they generally occur in the atmosphere. The mean heights given refer to temperate latitudes and it has to be remembered that in particular cases great departures from these heights may occur. For example, in polar regions cirrus may be almost on the ground.

FAMILY A : HIGH CLOUDS

(Usually above 6,000 metres)

1. Cirrus
2. Cirrocumulus
3. Cirrostratus

68

FAMILY B : MIDDLE CLOUDS
(Usually between 2,000 and 6,000 metres)
    4.   Altocumulus
    5.   Altostratus

FAMILY C : LOW CLOUDS
(Usually below 2,000 metres)
    6.   Stratocumulus
    7.   Stratus
    8.   Nimbostratus

FAMILY D : CLOUDS WITH VERTICAL DEVELOPMENT
(Mean upper level that of the cirrus, mean lower level 500 metres)
    9.   Cumulus
    10.   Cumulonimbus

These names do not by any means exhaust the varieties of clouds which experienced observers may detect and classify. Many transitional forms exist between these typical forms, and for more detailed information than can be given here the reader is referred to the Atlas of the International Meteorological Committee, or to such works as G. A. Clarke's *Clouds*. Definitions and descriptions of the chief types, as officially adopted in the International Atlas, are given below, together with some information as to the conditions under which the various types most commonly occur. The recognized abbreviations are given in brackets after each name.

CIRRUS (CI.)

The word in Latin means literally " a curl of hair ", and is applied to detached clouds of delicate and fibrous appearance, without shading, generally white in colour, often of a silky appearance.

Cirrus appears in the most varied forms, such as isolated tufts, lines drawn across a blue sky, branching feather-like plumes, curved lines ending in tufts, etc. ; they are often arranged in bands which cross the sky like meridian lines, and which, owing to the effect of perspective, converge to a point on the horizon, or to two opposite points.

Cirrus clouds are always composed of ice crystals, and are usually so thin that they may cross the sun's disc without dimming its light much. Occasionally, however, they may be so thick as to veil the light and obliterate the contour of the sun. Halos are rather rare in cirrus. Cirrus of the very delicate type is an indication of a very distant disturbance which will usually not affect the weather for some time.

Before sunrise and after sunset, cirrus is sometimes coloured bright yellow or red. These clouds are lit up long before other clouds and fade out much later ; sometimes after sunset they become grey.

Cirrus, being in general more or less inclined to the horizontal, tends less than other clouds to become parallel to the horizon, under the effect of perspective, as the horizon is approached ; often on the contrary, as already mentioned, it seems to converge to a point on the horizon. This type occurs in front of a typical depression. Cirrus quite frequently appears in the form of a comma, the upper part ending in a little tuft or point ; this type also often occurs in front of a typical depression.

Another kind of cirrus, usually called hybrid cirrus, either proceeds from or has originated from the anvil of a cumulonimbus (referred to later). It is met with either in the rear of a depression or in connection with thunderstorms.

CIRROCUMULUS (CICU.)

This type is defined as a cirriform layer or patch composed of small white flakes or of very small globular masses, without shadows, which are arranged in groups or lines, or more often in ripples resembling those of the sand on the seashore.

Real cirrocumulus is somewhat uncommon and it usually represents a degraded state of cirrus and cirrostratus. Indeed, an essential characteristic of the cloud, according to the latest definition, is its association with cirrus or cirrostratus. It is found on the front or the sides of a shallow disturbance, or on the edges of anticyclones, and plays a varied part in popular prognostics. We have, for example :

> " If woolly fleeces spread the heavenly way,
> Be sure no rain disturbs the summer's day."

Or the provincial French saying, " El ciel pecoun promête un bel matin ". But, on the other hand, Virgil (*Georgics*, i, 397) considers it a sign of rain if it should happen that—

> " Tenuia . . . lanæ per cælum vellera ferri."

And so in the neighbourhood of Pisa they say : " Cielo a pecorelle, Acqua a catinelle " ; and in the Tyrol : " Sind Morgens Himmelschäflein, wird's Nachmittags hageln oder schnei'n " ; and in France they have the proverb contrary to the one we have first quoted :—

> " Temps pommelé, fille fardée,
> Ne sont pas de longue durée."

The term " dappled sky " (ciel pommelé) is a little equivocal, and might refer to the other form of cirrocumulus, known in Northern Europe as " mackerel sky ".

Anyhow, we have to reconcile an apparently contradictory set of prognostics. The reason appears to be that in Northern Europe rain is chiefly cyclonic, and therefore rarely preceded by fleecy cirrocumulus, so that the appearance of that cloud denotes the edge of an anticyclone, and fine weather for a day at least. In Central and Southern Europe, on the contrary, fleecy clouds are usually formed in front of secondaries, thunderstorms, and non-isobaric rains, so that their cirrocumulus is a sign of approaching rain.

Cirrostratus (Cist.)

This type consists of a thin whitish veil, which does not blur the outlines of the sun or moon, but gives rise to halos. Sometimes it is quite diffuse and merely gives the sky a milky look ; sometimes it more or less distinctly shows a fibrous structure with disordered filaments.

A milky veil of fog is distinguished from a veil of cirrostratus of a similar appearance by the halo phenomena which the sun or the moon nearly always produce in a layer of cirrostratus, more especially of the kind found immediately in front of the central area of a depression.

What has been said above of the transparent character and colours of cirrus is true to a great extent of cirrostratus. In cases where the veil of cirrostratus reaches the horizon in one direction but leaves a segment of sky clear in the other direction, it may be regarded as indicating the northern edge of a disturbance.

Altocumulus (Acu.)

Altocumulus occurs as a layer, or patches composed of lamina or rather flattened globular masses, the smallest elements of the regularly arranged layer being fairly small and thin, with or without shading. These elements are arranged in groups, in lines, or waves, following one or two directions, and are sometimes so close together that their edges join.

The thin and semi-transparent edges of the elements often show irisations which are rather characteristic of this class of cloud and are a sure indication that the cloud is altocumulus and not cirrocumulus or stratocumulus. Also, if a thin semi-transparent patch of altocumulus passes in front of the sun or moon a corona appears. The corona is a series of coloured rings immediately surrounding the sun or moon, the inner bluish white, the outer brownish red, the series sometimes being repeated once or twice.

The corona is produced by diffraction of the light by water-drops and the radius of the ring is inversely proportional to the size of the drops.

A halo differs from a corona in its formation in that the halo is due to refraction of light through ice crystals and it has the opposite colour sequence in its rings. The very frequently seen halo has a radius of 22°. A halo of 46° radius can occasionally be seen, but it is seldom complete.

In tropical and subtropical regions a layer of altocumulus often forms at the end of the night in quiet weather and in the absence of any disturbance. In temperate latitudes the type is most often found on the south side or south front of a depression.

ALTOSTRATUS (AST.)

This type is defined as a striated veil, more or less grey or bluish in colour. The cloud is like thick cirrostratus, but without halo phenomena ; the sun or moon shows vaguely, with a faint gleam, as though through ground glass. Sometimes the sheet is thin, with forms intermediate with cirrostratus. Sometimes it is very thick and dark, sometimes even completely hiding the sun or moon. In this case differences of thickness may cause relatively light patches between very dark parts ; but the surface never shows real relief, and the striated or fibrous structure is always seen in places in the body of the cloud.

Every form is observed between high altostratus and cirrostratus on the one hand, and low altostratus and nimbostratus on the other.

Rain or snow may fall from altostratus (altostratus precipitans), but when the rain is heavy the cloud layer will have grown thicker and lower, becoming nimbostratus ; but heavy snow may fall from a layer that is definitely altostratus.

The cloud is typical of the central part of a depression.

Stratocumulus (Stcu.)

With stratocumulus we come to the lower clouds. It is defined as a layer or patches composed of lamina or globular masses ; the smallest of the regularly arranged elements are fairly large ; they are soft and grey, with darker parts.

These elements are arranged in groups, in lines, or in waves, aligned in one or in two directions. Very often the rolls are so close that their edges join together ; when they cover the whole sky, as on the Continent, especially in winter, they have a very wavy appearance.

There are transitional forms between stratocumulus and altocumulus, and, in fact, the cloud sheet noted as altocumulus by an observer at a small height would appear as stratocumulus to an observer at a greater height.

Also stratocumulus may change into stratus and vice versa.

Common forms are roll cumulus or stratocumulus undulatus and the festooned type, stratocumulus mammatus, the latter appearing sometimes in the rear of a disturbance or after showers or thunder.

Sometimes at the end of the day stratocumulus is formed by the settling down and flattening of the daytime cumulus clouds.

In winter stratocumulus occurs frequently in anticyclones, or in the relatively high pressure areas between depressions.

Stratus (St.)

Stratus is a uniform layer of cloud, resembling fog, but not resting on the ground. The same cloud, if broken up into irregular pieces is known as fractostratus.

If a layer of stratus is thin it gives the sky a misty appearance and some drizzle may occasionally fall from it.

Stratus occurs most usually outside the region of a disturbance or on the extreme edges of one, or in an anticyclone.

NIMBOSTRATUS (NBST.)

This is defined as a low, amorphous, and rainy layer, of a dark grey colour and nearly uniform ; feebly illuminated seemingly from within. When it gives precipitation it is in the form of continuous rain or snow which, however, may not actually reach the ground.

This kind of cloud usually evolves from a layer of altostratus by the latter becoming thicker, and developing beneath it low ragged clouds which gradually merge together into a continuous layer. The process is characteristic of the front of the central area of a depression.

CUMULUS (CU.)

Cumulus is a thick cloud with vertical development ; the upper surface is dome-shaped and exhibits protuberances, while the base is nearly horizontal.

Seen against the sun these clouds look dark unless at the edges, but when illuminated they are bright and white. They are typical developments of bright days when the lapse rate of temperature in the vertical direction is sufficiently steep for insolation to lead readily to strong convectional effects. From the method of formation of clouds of the cumulus type, it might be supposed that the temperature in such clouds would always be rather higher than the temperature in the surrounding air at the same level. Actually C. K. M. Douglas has found that the temperature in these clouds is sometimes lower than in the surrounding air, and he explains this on the supposition that, in these cases, the rising mass of air has probably been carried up past its equilibrium position by momentum gained in a lower layer where its position was definitely an unstable one. Another possibility that has been advanced is that the cloud mass indicates merely the top of a long column of rising air and that it is this column as a whole that is lighter than surrounding columns. This latter explanation of the origin of clouds of the cumulus type has the merit also of accounting for the spreading-out effects which lead to the formation of the " anvils " occasionally associated with cumulonimbus under conditions of extreme instability.

Cumulus clouds vary from the soft edged clouds of fine weather to the hard edged " cauliflower " type, heavy and swelling, characteristic of showery weather or days with a thundery tendency.

CUMULONIMBUS (CUNB.)

These are heavy masses of cloud, with great vertical development, whose cumuliform summits rise in the form of mountains or towers, the upper parts having a fibrous texture and often spreading out in the shape of an anvil. They are generally connected with showers of rain or snow and sometimes hail and thunderstorms. The official distinction between cumulus and cumulonimbus is that in the latter the whole or part of their tops is in process of transformation into cirroform masses or in some cases into an " anvil ". Cumulonimbus has been described as a factory of clouds. It is of frequent occurrence in the rear of a disturbance.

CLOUD OBSERVATION

It is characteristic of the modern system of observing and reporting weather that it recognizes the necessity of noting the appearance of the sky as a whole rather than of merely listing the different forms of cloud seen. A special " state-of-the-sky " code has been devised for the purpose, and regarding the observations the international instructions run as follow :—

" Each specification of the code corresponds to a state of the sky, lower, middle, or high. . . . The detailed analysis of the individual clouds should follow and not precede this recognition of the state of the sky as a whole. If the observer gets used to this course he will find in a short time that the different states of the sky, lower, middle and high, corresponding with the code, will seem just as 'live' as the typical cloud forms, and it will be just as easy to identify a state of the sky as the form of a cloud.

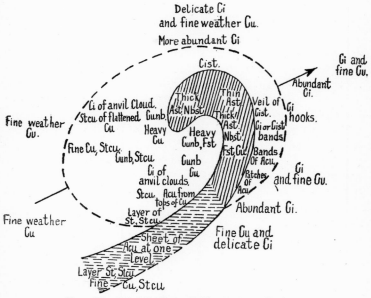

FIG. 11.—Distribution of Clouds in a Cyclone.

" The aspect of the sky is continually changing, and many transitional forms exist between the different types of cloud described in the Atlas. It is relatively rare for the observer to see typical clouds of one genus which float past, or persist in the sky for any considerable time ; in most cases he will find that he has difficulties at the time of observation if he has not taken the trouble to watch the sky since the last observation. If however he has taken this precaution he will often be able to refer a confusing state of the sky, or a particular cloud, to a previous state which was typical and easy to identify. Moreover, most of the specifications of the cloud code take into account the evolution of the clouds. A single isolated observation is insufficient.

" As regards evolution, the recognition of the state of the sky as a whole, recommended in the previous paragraph, is better than the identification of clouds considered by themselves, for as a matter of fact the evolution of the state of the sky can be followed indefinitely at one station, while the evolution of a cloud, if, as is usual, it is a ' migrant ' can only be observed during the relatively short time that it takes to cross the sky."

Fig. 11, which has been adapted from an illustration in the International Atlas, indicates the average distribution of cloud in a typical depression in Western Europe.

Figs. 12 to 21 are photographs of skies typical of the various meteorological situations indicated in the descriptions attached to the figures. All of these photographs were taken at Aberdeen by Mr. G. A. Clarke, to whom the writer is indebted for permission to publish the photographs.

Clouds at Great Altitudes

All the clouds to which we have so far referred lie in the troposphere. At somewhat rare intervals clouds have been observed at very much greater heights. These very high clouds appear to be of two types, the first in the stratosphere at heights of between 20 and 30 km., the second type at the much greater height of about 80 km.

Clouds of the first type were first noted by Mohn and were called by him mother-of-pearl clouds. They were seen also by Professor Carl Störmer in 1890. They again appeared in Scandinavia in January and February, 1932, and on a number of occasions were photographed by

Professor Störmer and his assistants. Fig. 22, from a photograph kindly supplied by Professor Störmer, shows the mother-of-pearl clouds seen from Oslo towards West after sunset on 19th February, 1932. The clouds seen in the figure were photographed from several of the stations operated by Professor Störmer in connection with the determination of the height of aurora ; and from the photographs and measurements so obtained Professor Störmer has estimated that the clouds lay at a height of between 21 and 25 km. On the same evening he made an observation from which it is possible to obtain some idea as to the nature of these clouds. He noted, around the moon, part of a large corona of which the inner radius was some 14° to 15° and of which the outer radius (a red ring) was estimated to be equal to or greater than 18°. From this last observation he computed that the cloud particles had diameters not exceeding 0·0025 millimetres.

The second type of very high clouds was noted, and their heights were estimated, by O. Jesse during the years 1885 to 1891. For these clouds he found the astonishing height of about 82 km. Since then the clouds have been seen several times in both hemispheres and always in the summer months at the place of observation. In July, 1932, Professor Störmer saw clouds of this type again and was able to photograph them from his auroral stations. Fig. 23 is from a photograph obtained by him on 27th July, 1909, and kindly lent to the writer.

These clouds are like cirrus, but have a shining bluish-white silvery colour and appear some hours after sunset or before sunrise. The average height of the clouds photographed by Professor Störmer was found to be 81 km., but he does not consider that definite conclusions can yet be drawn as to the nature of these clouds. Though seen some hours after the time of sunset (or before the time of sunrise) on the earth's surface at the time of observation, these clouds are at so great a height as to be still illuminated by the rays of the sun ; and it is estimated that the rays which illuminate these clouds pass through the earth's atmosphere at a minimum distance of 30 to 60 km. from the surface of the earth.

BIBLIOGRAPHY

International Atlas of Clouds and of States of the Sky. Paris : Office National Météorologique.
Clouds. G. A. Clarke. London : Constable & Co.
Height and Velocity of Luminous Night-Clouds observed in Norway, 1932. Carl Störmer. Univ. of Oslo Pubn., No. 6.

FIG. 12. Sky showing first appearance of Cirrus in the west after spell of fine weather—depression approaching. Cirrus and Cirrostratus above, Stratocumulus below.

FIG. 13. Sky indicative of approach of depression. Cirrus tufted and in lines, increasing with time.

[face p. 80

FIG. 14. Sky in depression—Altostratus above with growing Nimbus below.

FIG. 15. Sky during passage of a " cold front " (minor line squall). Mass of turbulent Nimbus or Cumulonimbus.

FIG. 16. Sky after a depression has entirely passed away. Clear sky (at evening) with detached and dispersing Stratocumulus.

FIG. 17. Sky of winter anticyclonic gloom.—Stratocumulus, extended and unbroken.

FIG. 18. Sky in South-westerly weather. Fractocumulus and lenticular banks of Altocumulus.

FIG. 19. Sky in Westerly weather—long bands of Cirrus, Cirrocumulus, and Altocumulus, lenticular Altocumulus below. Weather usually changeable.

FIG. 20. Sky of Northerly and North-westerly weather of unsettled type, squally, showers of rain and hail. Massive Cumulonimbus and Fractonimbus.

FIG. 21. Sky of thundery weather—massive bank of Cumulonimbus.

FIG. 22. Mother-of-pearl clouds seen from Oslo towards West after sunset on February 19th, 1932.

FIG. 23. Luminous night clouds, July 27th, 1909.

CHAPTER V

STRUCTURE OF CYCLONES

DISCONTINUITIES

THE broad features of a cyclone and its wind and weather have already been described in the second chapter. The picture drawn was a general one, and mainly from the prognostic point of view ; it is now possible to proceed to diagnosis and to fill in a good deal of the detail. The present chapter is intended to deal largely with the structure of a cyclone according to present day ideas. It has to be remarked that on one point there is a distinct difference between present day ideas and those commonly in vogue at the time when the general picture of the second chapter was drawn by Abercromby almost fifty years ago. The difference arises in the prominence given nowadays to the idea of " discontinuities ". The idea is not a new one ; it bulked largely in the meteorological theory of Dove and others rather over seventy years ago. The technical sense in which the word is now used in meteorology is best explained by an example. Suppose, for example, the temperature at Edinburgh is 40° F and at London 50° F. In the absence of more detailed information one is most inclined to assume that in the region between these places the temperature changes gradually and continuously from 40° to 50°. On weather maps, however, cases are found where the temperature changes abruptly or at least very rapidly as one crosses a certain line or narrow zone. For example, the temperature distribution in the above-mentioned case might be such that everywhere northward of a line joining Glasgow to Newcastle the temperature is not greatly different from 40°, whilst everywhere southward of that line the temperature is not greatly different from 50°. The dividing line would then be called a line of discontinuity. The speed and direction of the wind would also probably change markedly as one crossed this line.

The idea of discontinuities was never perhaps entirely absent from meteorological thought ; the reader, indeed, will appreciate that the squall line of Abercromby's diagram (Fig. 3) answers to the description of a line of discontinuity, and that the curved dotted line drawn from the centre beyond the word " muggy " to the word " gloomy " suggests another line of discontinuity, at least of wind.

THE POLAR FRONT

The importance of discontinuities in the anatomy of a cyclone was first brought out by the Bergen School of meteorologists working under Professor V. Bjerknes. During the War the Norwegians developed a close network of meteorological stations in their own country, and made a study of the detailed synoptic charts which it thus became possible to construct. The result showed that discontinuities were as a rule present in cyclones and it led to the announcement of the " polar front " theory, according to which the cyclones develop as waves in the bounding surface between two currents or moving masses of air of different characteristics and different origins. Since these air masses usually come from polar and sub-tropical regions respectively, they are generally termed polar air and tropical or equatorial air, but also sometimes simply cold air and warm air, the terms being used throughout in a relative sense. To emphasize this point and to indicate the difference between tropical and polar air in various seasons of the year we introduce below a table of temperatures. The values given in the table are the means derived from observations made during a period of only sixteen months, but they suffice to illustrate a number of points.

TABLE III

MEAN TEMPERATURES (IN ° F) AT SURFACE-LEVEL AND AT 1,000 FT. AND THEREAFTER AT VARIOUS PRESSURES IN THE UPPER AIR, IN " TROPICAL AIR " (T) AND IN " POLAR AIR " (P)

(Results deduced from observations made during Aeroplane Ascents in the British Isles in the period September, 1921–December, 1922)

Month	Surface		1,000 ft.		Pressure in Millibars									
					900		800		700		600		500	
	T	P	T	P	T	P	T	P	T	P	T	P	T	P
Jan.	49	40	47	37	39	31	30	20	18	8	5	— 6	—	— 21
Feb.	—	43	47	40	44	33	37	23	28	11	13	— 7	—	—
Mar.	50	42	45	38	41	29	34	19	22	9	11	— 4	—	—
Apr.	—	50	—	41	—	34	—	23	—	14	—	— 1	—	—
May	66	47	63	38	55	31	45	24	34	16	20	4	5	—
June	65	48	63	48	57	38	45	29	34	20	21	8	—	—
July	59	57	55	53	50	45	46	33	37	25	24	14	—	—
Aug.	58	55	55	52	46	44	44	34	34	27	27	14	—	— 6
Sept.	60	55	57	51	51	43	45	35	37	25	24	14	—	—
Oct.	59	51	57	47	51	38	44	30	33	22	21	10	3	— 5
Nov.	49	40	48	39	43	31	35	21	27	12	17	4	—	— 8
Dec.	49	40	47	38	43	32	37	24	28	13	16	1	1	—

First of all we note the great difference of temperature in the months of May and June, and more especially in May, between air masses of different origins. Everyone will recall that in these months in various years any kind of weather has been experienced from great heat on the one hand, to the type on the other hand in which snow appears on the higher mountains. These extremes correspond to the extremes of tropical air and the extremes of polar air respectively, but even between the average specimens of air masses of the different kinds there is in these months a mean difference of temperature of the order of 20° F.

As the summer advances this difference in temperature becomes almost obliterated, so that in July and August, at least at lower heights, polar air by the time it reaches the British Isles is almost as warm as tropical air. In the upper air, however, the difference of temperature remains substantial, and this, as we note elsewhere, betokens a degree of considerable instability in the polar air.

In autumn the difference of temperature between polar and tropical air becomes substantial at all levels.

Another point of interest is that the presence of polar

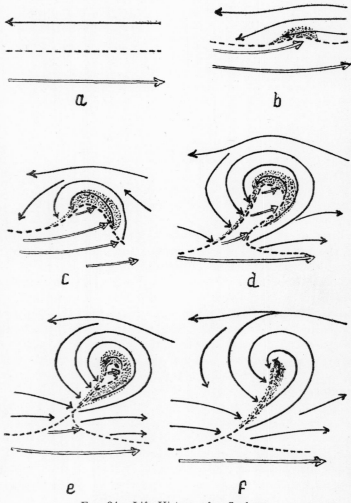

Fig. 24.—Life History of a Cyclone.

air in our islands in May and June means as a rule actually
slightly colder weather (unless perhaps for an hour or two
in the middle of the day) than the presence of equatorial
air in the midwinter months. This illustrates in a striking
way the variability of climate in our country, a variability
so great as at times to annul seasonal differences ; and it
gives point to the saying that the British climate comprises
specimens of many climates.

It will be noted that within the levels considered tropical
air shows no negative temperatures, but polar air, by the
time a pressure of 600 mb. is reached, passes to the negative
side of the Fahrenheit scale in winter and spring months.
This is one of the points of inconvenience which may be
avoided when upper air temperatures are expressed on the
Absolute scale.

The line of separation between the two air masses is
called the " polar front " ; the bounding surface between
the two masses is very far from vertical and, indeed, usually
slopes upward—in the direction of the cold air—at a slope
of about 1 : 100.

The life history of a cyclone according to the Bergen
theory is set out briefly in the diagrams a, b, c, d, e, f of
Fig. 24. In the initial stage (diagram a) we have the two
currents, the polar flowing as a rule from east or north-east
and the equatorial from west or south-west. The polar air
is to be regarded as filling a wedge-shaped space, the edge
of the wedge being the Polar Front, represented by the
dotted line. The arrangement of two currents in this way is
not one which can long persist ; any slight disturbance of
the surface of separation tends to develop. The first step
in the formation of a cyclone is a slight bulge of the surface
to northward as in diagram b, which rapidly develops to
the stage c. The stage c represents what is known as a young
and active cyclone, whose centre is at the northward tip of
the tongue of warm air.

Vertical sections and a larger scale plan of this cyclone
are shown in Fig. 25. It will be seen that along that part

of the polar front marked "Warm Front" the warm air is rising as a south-westerly current over the cold air, which is here a southerly current. On the other hand, along the part which is called the "Cold Front" the cold air, as

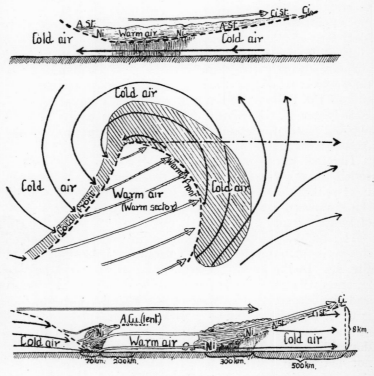

FIG. 25.—Vertical and horizontal sections of an idealized cyclone.

a north-westerly current, is advancing like a wedge under the warm south-westerly current.

The dimensions marked on the lowest diagram of Fig. 25 do not, of course, apply to individual cyclones, which vary greatly; they are intended only to give the reader an idea of the scale of events in an average case.

WEATHER AT THE FRONTS

It will be observed that in this chapter the word " front " is being used no longer as meaning the whole forward part of the cyclone, but is used in the sense of being the forward edge of the warm air or the cold air as the case may be. The important advance connected with the Bergen theory of cyclones lies in the recognition of the close association of the weather with these fronts. The region of rainfall is indicated in Fig. 25 by shading. Fig 25 shows the warm air at the warm front rising upward over the wedge of cold air. The warm air is generally fairly humid and after it has risen one or two thousand feet cloud will begin to form. As the ascent continues the cloud becomes denser and the waterdrops begin to fall out as rain. Thus over a considerable belt to north-eastward of the warm front rain will be falling through the wedge of cold air. Rain produced in this way is similar to rain produced by the rising of a warm moist current up a mountain side, the only difference being that in the cyclone the wedge of cold air plays the part of the mountain. The rain produced at the warm front is of a fairly continuous type, and may last for several hours.

As a rule rain also occurs at the cold front, but in this case it is in the form of showers, sometimes heavy. It is not so evident why there should be rain at the cold front, because there is frequently considerable downward movement of the warm air in this region. The motion, however, is somewhat complex. The warm air above the wedge is moving from south-west. The cold air in the wedge is moving as a rule from north-west to south-east, and is cutting south-eastward under the warm current. Near the forward edge there is frequently considerable and sometimes violent upward movement in the warm air, and the whole change from warm to cold takes place abruptly and in squall-like manner. Thus the cold front is frequently called the squall-line. The matter of the instability in the region of squall-lines is referred to further in the chapter on Line Squalls.

If reference be now made to the vertical section in Fig. 25 as envisaged by the Norwegian meteorologists, it will be seen that the sequence of events in that picture as a cyclone passes agrees closely in many respects with the sequence as described by Abercromby and as illustrated in the cloud photographs. Thus the first sign of the advancing depression is the Cirrus cloud, then the Cirrostratus, with perhaps a halo round the sun, next the Altostratus cloud or watery sky, and then the Nimbus and the rain of the warm front. At this point, however, the Bergen picture has an additional feature, namely, the warm sector, a region of warm air, generally cloudy, but as a rule without rain of any importance. The muggy part with the Stratocumulus cloud in Abercromby's picture most nearly resembles the warm sector in weather. Finally, from the cold front— Abercromby's trough line of squalls or clearing showers— the two pictures again agree.

The rainfall at fronts is subject to some variation according to locality and time of day. These matters are treated in the chapters on local and diurnal variations respectively.

OCCLUSION OF THE WARM SECTOR

Having now described the young and vigorous cyclone we must return to Fig. 24 and consider the next stage in its development. As a rule the cold front advances more rapidly than the warm front, and the result is that the warm sector is gradually surrounded and finally lifted off the ground. This stage is known as the " occlusion ", and the line in diagram f along which the cold and warm fronts join up is called the " line of occlusion ". The warm air is still present, but it is higher up in the atmosphere. It will be realized that the depression in the surface region has now taken on practically the form of Abercromby's scheme. The depressions which reach the British Isles from the Atlantic

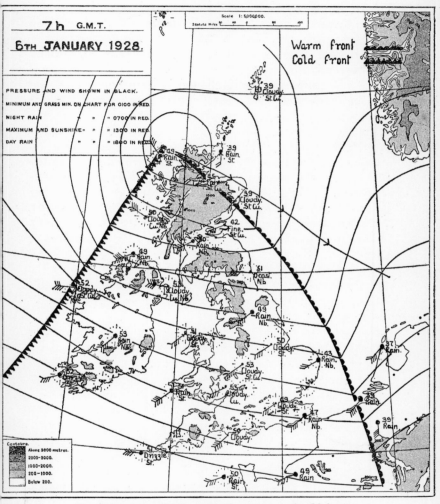

FIG. 26.—Synoptic chart showing warm and cold fronts.

are very often in the occluded stage, so that Abercromby's scheme applies to the majority of them.

The synoptic chart of Fig. 26 represents a depression analysed after the Bergen manner. The depression is centred near Lewis and the warm front runs from there south-eastward down the North Sea. The cold front runs in a S.S.W. direction, just skirting the coast of Ireland. It will be observed that the isobars have distinct discontinuities in their directions at both the warm and the cold fronts and that the isobars in the warm sector are comparatively straight. The corresponding discontinuities in wind and temperature are equally well marked. Thus in the cold air to the eastward of the warm front the isobars indicate a gradient for S.S.W. winds, whilst in the warm sector the gradient direction is roughly westerly, though most of the surface winds are somewhat inclined to this direction. In Fig. 26 (and also in Figs. 29, 56, and 66) the numbers of feathers on the arrows indicate the force of the wind according to the Beaufort scale. The temperatures in the cold air to eastward of the warm front are just under 40° F, whilst soon after the warm front is crossed they rise to about 50°.

On this chart we have no indication as to the temperatures beyond the cold front, but the chart for 18 h. of 6th January (not reproduced) indicates temperatures again of about or rather under 40° F over Scotland, and temperatures of the order of 45° F over a considerable part of England.

Reference should now be made to Fig. 10 in Chapter III, where we plotted the upper air temperatures at Duxford, near Cambridge, at 10 a.m. on 5th and 6th respectively. On the first of these dates the ascent took place in the polar air lying between this depression and one which preceded it ; on the second date the ascent took place in the tropical air of the warm sector of the depression of 6th January. At the 1,000 millibar level the temperature on the second day is about 12° warmer than on the first day, and at the 850 millibar level (i.e. nearly 5,000 feet above mean sea level) the temperature on the second day is about 23° warmer than on the first day. Incidentally, the lapse rate in the polar air in the first 5,000 feet is much steeper than in the tropical air. This difference between tropical and polar air is characteristic ; it indicates a greater degree of instability and of turbulence in the polar air in the levels considered, and it is a matter to which we make reference again as bearing on the weather experienced on days characterized by polar and tropical air respectively.

The direction of movement of the centre of the depression in the period subsequent to the time to which the chart relates is indicated by the line marked with arrow-heads, and it will be noted that it is approximately the same as the direction of the isobars of the warm sector.

Some further details regarding this particular depression are given in the next chapter.

These features are characteristic of a young and vigorous depression ; in a dying depression there is a closer approach to symmetry about a centre.

OTHER THEORIES AND OTHER CONSIDERATIONS

The Bergen theory gives a very good picture of the actual structure of a cyclone. This does not necessarily prove, however, that the theory, in so far as it ascribes an origin or cause for depressions, is correct. If cyclones do originate as waves in a sloping boundary surface between warm and cold currents their structure would doubtless be very much as we find it to be. On the other hand, the discontinuities might be the effect rather than the cause of the depression ; and other explanations of the structure and in particular of the discontinuities have been advanced. Suppose that we have initially in temperate regions an arrangement of the atmosphere in which temperature decreases gradually from south to north, that is, the isotherms run from west to east ; then if a horizontal circular whirl be set up some-how in such a region one can picture the isotherms as being twisted round so that there is a warm patch in the right front and a cold patch in the rear, i.e. the result is broadly to produce a structure of the Bergen description. According to this idea, however, the lines of discontinuity are the effect, rather than the cause of the cyclonic motion.

Another idea for which a good deal can be said is known as the Exner barrier theory. According to Exner, given a discontinuity, the cyclone may originate not as a wave, but rather by reason of a promontory of cold air flowing out southward from the main cold mass and acting like a barrier across the path of the warm westerly current. The effect of the barrier is to cause a heaping up of the atmosphere (i.e. an anticyclone or wedge) to its west side and a deficiency (i.e. a depression) to its east side.

Again, it has been suggested that the instantaneous movement of air in a cyclone can frequently be described as that of a core of air rotating like a solid (i.e. with speed proportional to distance from centre) and surrounded by a region in which the air speed varies inversely with distance from centre ; thus on this picture a depression consists of a solid rotating core surrounded by a " simple vortex ".

The conception of a solid core and a surrounding vortex provides a possible explanation of the persistence and stability of cyclonic motion, more especially in the later and prolonged stage when the cyclone has ceased to bear any resemblance to a wave.

At the same time we must guard against the idea of supposing that the cyclone can be regarded as a sort of travelling and rotating disc consisting always of the *same* air masses. There are conclusive reasons against such a supposition. If this were really the case, we ought to be able to get the actual air motion by compounding the rotational and translational motions of any particle of air in the usual manner ; but when we do so, we find usually that we get winds different from what are actually observed, at least at the surface. Take that portion of the front of a cyclone where the wind from rotation would be south, and suppose it to be compounded with even a slow motion of translation towards the east, then the resulting wind must have a component from the west—that is to say, it would blow outwards in front of the centre. Now, this is exactly what it does not do. Observation shows that the wind is at times more incurved in front of a cyclone than in any other portion, and therefore the idea of a rotating disc consisting always of the same air cannot be maintained. We are thus rather compelled to believe that a cyclone-vortex is propagated in a manner somewhat analogous to a wave or eddy of water. When a wave approaches the shore, the first impulse is always an indraught, though, of course, the motion of the wave is forwards ; and when a cyclone approaches, the first impulse is likewise inwards. It is the system of circulation that travels, new air being continually drawn in along the surface in one direction and expelled in another direction, some of it probably upwards. A great deal of light was thrown on air movements in a memoir on *Life History of Surface Air Currents*, by Sir Napier Shaw and Mr. R. G. K. Lempfert. We return to this question in the chapter on hurricanes and revolving storms.

When we come to consider cyclones in different parts of the world we find the typical shape of isobars to be oval with the inner isobars usually closer to the rear than to the front ; and the rain extends further before than behind the trough. But the tropical cyclone has a striking feature which is absent in our latitudes. There is a patch of blue sky over the calm centre, which is well known in the hurricane countries as the " eye of the storm ", or as a " bull's-eye ". Then cirrus and halo appear all round a tropical cyclone, while they are not seen in the immediate rear of a European storm ; and though the way in which the rain seems to grow out of the air in front of a cyclone is the same everywhere, the sky and clouds in rear of a hurricane are much softer and dirtier than in temperate cyclones. There is not that sharp difference between the quality of clouds in front and rear which is so striking in higher latitudes. Still greater is the absence of any marked squall or change of weather during the passage of the trough in the tropics—that is, at the moment when the barometer begins to turn upwards. Some who study hurricanes have scarcely noticed any change then ; and all are agreed that the trough-phenomena are very slight.

We have already shown, in the chapter on the prognostic aspects, that a cyclone has, as it were, a double symmetry. One set of phenomena, such as wind, cloud, and rain, are grouped round the centre ; while the second set, such as the different character of the temperature and clouds in front and rear, and the line of squalls along the line where the barometer begins to rise, are related to the trough of the cyclone. If we call the first set the rotational, and the second set the translational, phenomena of a cyclone, we find that the former are all more marked in the tropical and the latter in extra-tropical cyclones. Then, if we examine the charts of cyclones, we see that, while tropical hurricanes are much smaller and have much stronger winds than any others, they only move from 2 to 10 miles an hour ; while extra-tropical cyclones rotate much more slowly, but are propagated at a rate of from 20 to 70 miles an hour.

Thus we might readily suppose that what we call rotational phenomena are really connected with the circulation, and the translational phenomena with the forward motion, of the cyclone. There is another point, namely, that the character of cloud and weather depends on the position relative to the front of a cyclone, and not on the direction of the wind. Cyclones in Europe move towards the east, and the dirty sky comes with a south-east wind ; while in the northern tropics hurricanes move towards the west, and the same sky comes with a north-west wind. People sometimes say that of course the rear of a cyclone must be clear, because of a cold dry north-west wind, but when a cyclone moves west, even in Europe, that wind becomes close and dirty.

SECONDARY DEPRESSIONS

It is one of the rules of the Bergen theory that the direction of motion of a cyclone is that of the isobars of the warm sector ; that, in Europe, as has just been said, usually means an eastward movement. The most frequent direction is about E.N.E., though in the example of Fig. 26 it happens that the direction is E.S.E. In cases where the cyclone becomes occluded and dies, it usually ceases to move much and an interesting development occurs, namely, the birth of a secondary ; the point where the cold front catches up the warm front generally becomes the centre of the secondary,

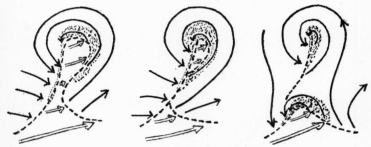

FIG. 27.—Formation of a secondary depression.

and, as will be seen from Fig. 27, the secondary will usually have its own warm front and cold front.

The various features of secondaries have already been described. Whilst resembling primary depressions in a general way, the secondaries usually have more consistently bad weather. A secondary depression may in turn become occluded and yet another depression may form to south-ward of it. A not uncommon sequence of events is for a primary depression to pass with centre between Iceland and Scotland, for an occlusion to occur with formation of a new centre at (say) the south of Ireland, then another in the Bay of Biscay, and finally yet another in the Gulf of Lyons.

V-shaped Depressions

An interesting shape of isobars to which the name
V-shaped depressions is given is that in which the isobars
are shaped like the letter V and enclose an area of low
pressure. In the northern hemisphere the point of the V is
usually directed towards the south, so that the wind is from
a southerly point in front and from west to north-west in
rear of the trough. The trough line is given at once by joining

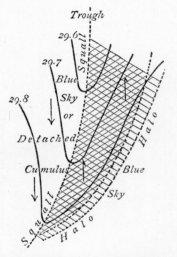

Fig. 28.—Weather in V-depression.

the southern points of each successive isobar, and in practice
is nearly always curved, the convexity being turned towards
the east, as in the diagram, Fig. 28. As the V is usually
moving towards the east, this line marks out the position of
all the places at which the barometer, having fallen more or
less, has just turned to rise, and it is called the " trough "
of the V.

These features are common to all V's, but the position of
the rain divides these depressions into two distinct types. For

actually these V's are as a rule associated either with the warm front or the cold front of a large depression and the weather will be determined accordingly.   In the case of the warm front type the rain area in front may be fairly broad and may give place to mild, cloudy weather behind.   In the case of the cold front type there will be the sharp clearing showers, with squall and cooler conditions in the rear.   It may happen, however, that the V is simply the trough or line of occlusion of an occluded depression, and in this case though the change of wind at the time of passage of the trough is marked, there will be little change of temperature. V's are sometimes formed in the col between two anti-cyclones.

DEPRESSIONS IN POLAR AIR

Depressions occasionally form apparently entirely within polar air and in circumstances in which, so far as can be

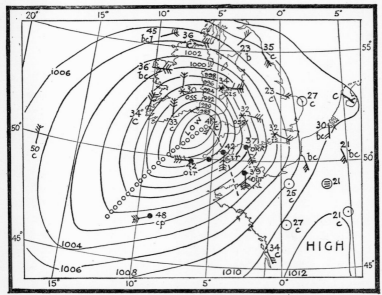

FIG. 29.—Synoptic chart 7th February, 1933, Quasi warm front ---- and Quasi cold front ° ° ° ° of depression in polar air.

H

seen, air of equatorial origin plays no part. A somewhat typical case is illustrated in Fig. 29, which appeared in the *Meteorological Magazine* of March, 1933, and is reproduced by the kind permission of the Director of the Meteorological Office.

On this chart a quasi-warm front and quasi-cold front are shown, but the air in the sector between them, though rather warmer than the polar air in the rest of the depression and relatively humid, was also of polar origin. It was, in fact, " maritime polar air " drawn from the Atlantic Ocean.

This depression, like many of its kind, moved in an irregular manner, not in the direction suggested by its warm sector, but actually westward. It was associated with snowstorms which, so far as the southern districts of the British Isles are concerned, were amongst the worst in living memory.

Depressions in polar air in winter and spring frequently give snowstorms.

COLS

The last shape of isobars which we have to describe is the " col ", or neck of low pressure, which lies between two adjacent anticyclones. In a most common case of European col a portion of one anticyclone lies over the Bay of Biscay, while another lies to the north-east of this over the Scandinavian peninsula. Then, while one area of comparatively low pressure lies to the north-west of Iceland, another covers Central Europe and the north of Italy, so that a saddle-back area, or neck, of low pressure is found over England. In the middle of the col there is no gradient, and therefore a calm, while all round the winds and weather conform to the usual law of isobars. The weather is dull, gloomy, and stagnant, and liable to be foggy in winter, while in summer thunderstorms are frequently found in different portions of a col.

As a whole no sequence of weather can be assigned to

a col. It does not move itself, but no law can be laid down to say whether the col will remain stationary or whether the area which it covers to-day will be occupied by some other type of pressure to-morrow.

The importance of this shape of isobars in forecasting arises from the fact that, as both the anticyclones are usually stationary, the col represents, as it were, a line of weakness, along which disturbances will be propagated.

Unfortunately, though a col can be safely forecast in

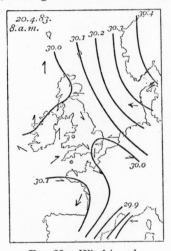

FIG. 30.—Wind in col.

general terms as for unsettled weather without much wind, the motion of cyclones as they meet a col is most uncertain. Sometimes they pass in a south-easterly direction across Europe between the two anticyclones, while more frequently the main body of the cyclone is deflected or dies out, while an irregular secondary pushes its way more or less across the col.

ORIGIN OF THE ISOBARIC FORMS

We have now, either in this chapter or in the third chapter, described the fundamental forms of isobars and a few remarks on the whole question will not be out of place here, though in the chapters on " Wind and Calm " and on " General Atmospheric Circulation " greater light is thrown on their significance.

We may take the analogy of water flowing in a river, with ripples and waves, backwaters and eddies of various sorts. In the eddying river the general cause of all motion is the downward current from the source to the mouth ; but water cannot slide like a solid weight on an inclined plane without forming horizontal and vertical whirls. In the atmosphere the source of all motion is the general circulation of air set up between the warm Equator and the cold poles. This air, like water, flows in a turbulent way, and isobars map out the varying pressure on the earth's surface induced by this uneven flow of air.

We must not, however, push the analogy too far ; to the extent, for example, of supposing that we have found a simple explanation of the cause of cyclones. And though we talk of isobars as if those lines were physical abstractions, all that we really do is to trace by their means the ever-changing disturbances in the flow of the atmosphere. We define these disturbances by certain abstract shapes of isobars and then, entirely from observation, we collate certain kinds of weather and sky with different portions of each isobaric configuration.

BIBLIOGRAPHY

Life Cycle of Cyclones and the Polar Front Theory of Atmospheric Circulation. J. Bjerknes and H. Solberg. Oslo : Geof. Pub., vol. iii, No. 1.

Chapter VI

ANEMOGRAMS, BAROGRAMS, THERMOGRAMS

Meteorogram of the Passage of a Depression

WE have already seen that a series of synoptic charts is, as it were, a series of bird's-eye views, not only of the appearance of the sky, but also of instrumental readings over a considerable area. These perhaps are taken at intervals of six hours, but we all know by experience that very great changes of weather may occur within that time. Also, as the stations from which the materials for making synoptic charts are derived are usually many miles apart, many of the details of a cyclone are lost. Every well-equipped observatory is therefore supplied with instruments which record or graph automatically the height of the barometer and of the thermometer, the direction and velocity of the wind, the occurrence and quantity of rain, the humidity of the air, and so on ; other instruments are sometimes added.

The trace marked on paper by a barograph is called a barogram ; that by a thermograph a thermogram ; both or either of the records left by the wind-instruments are called anemograms ; and if all or several of these are combined in one diagram, the whole is called a meteorogram, because it is a writing of meteorological instruments.

Fig. 31 is a copy of a set of simultaneous records taken at the telegraphic reporting station maintained on the Island of Tiree by the Meteorological Office. The records relate to the period from the afternoon of 5th January to the afternoon of 6th January, 1928.

The synoptic chart in Fig. 26 related to 7 h. of 6th January,

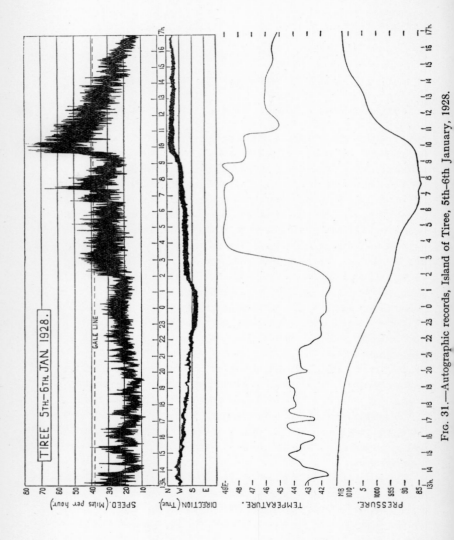

Fig. 31.—Autographic records, Island of Tiree, 5th–6th January, 1928.

1928, and to understand the meteorogram of Fig. 31 fully
we must recall that chart, which was considered in the last
chapter.   The chart indicated a well-marked depression
which moved on a course directed roughly from W.N.W.
to E.S.E. and whose centre crossed the Island of Lewis
about 7 h. on 6th January. Fig. 31 comprises in order from
top to bottom the records of wind speed, wind direction,
temperature, and pressure.

Looking first at the wind record we note that about 20 h.
on the 5th the wind at Tiree was S.S.W. in direction and
averaged about 16 m.p.h. in speed. The first sign of the
advancing depression is characteristic, namely, a backing
of the wind—in this case to S.S.E.—and a gradual increase
in strength. The temperature during this period begins at
about 43° F and falls to under 42°, and, in fact, the cold air
in front of the warm front is now flowing over the Island.
It will be noted also that pressure is falling.

About 1 h. certain marked changes begin to appear.
Wind veers, and in little over an hour the wind has changed
nearly to south-west and has risen in speed to a mean of
just over 30 m.p.h. The constancy in speed and direction
for some four hours thereafter should be noted ; the station
is now in the warm sector. Temperature rises rapidly for
nearly three hours despite the fact that this is near the
middle of the night and then remains fairly steady at about
49° F, whilst the rate of fall of pressure diminishes somewhat and then ceases.

A further set of changes, this time of a more complex
nature, begins shortly after 6 h. The wind begins to veer
and becomes highly variable in speed, taking on a squally
character. The change in direction to north-west is not
completed until nearly 10 a.m. Temperature falls abruptly
in at least three steps, despite the fact that it is now forenoon when ordinarily the temperature would rise ; when
these changes are almost concluded, i.e. about 10 h., pressure
begins to rise very steeply. This further set of changes is
associated with the passage of the cold front.   The change

from warm to cold sometimes takes place in one drop but the above way of changing by steps at the cold front is not uncommon.

In this particular depression the highest wind speeds of all occur at about 10 h., when the middle of the wind trace gets up to about 55 m.p.h. whilst the extreme gusts rise to about 80 m.p.h. The highest winds are frequently experienced at the cold front or squall line, but this is by no means always the case ; generally the wind speed falls fairly rapidly thereafter.

One of the most important uses of the traces of autographic instruments is in the study of the detailed structure of depressions ; and much of our knowledge of fronts, line squalls, etc., has been acquired by the patient collation of outstanding features of numerous records and their interpretation with the help of synoptic charts.

SUPERPOSITION OF VARIATIONS ON CURVES

Now the meteorogram we have dealt with is one on which considerable changes of weather, associated with the passage of a depression, are indicated. We use the word " changes " here in a definite sense ; the passage of a cyclone, or its replacement by an anticyclone, really changes the weather. But the weather and perhaps more obviously the temperature and wind may alter according to the time of day ; and to this type of alteration we apply the term " diurnal variation ". The traces of diurnal variation may more or less be masked by the greater changes due to cyclones ; in the case above we have deliberately, indeed, selected an example in which the temperature rises to its maximum at what is ordinarily the coldest time of the night, but it is important for anyone who would understand the weather—even the weather of cyclones—to know something about the diurnal variations of the various elements. For that reason we devote a later chapter entirely to the subject.

The actual weather is the sum or balance of various influences superposed one upon the other. As an example of the superposing of curves let us try to find out what would

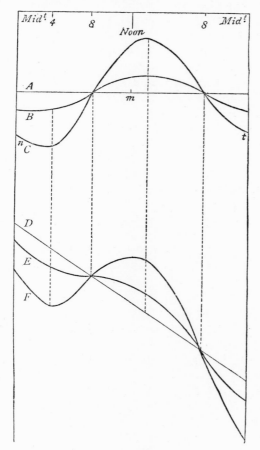

Fig. 32.—Superposition of Curves.

be the nature of the curve left by a thermograph if a regular diurnal variation of temperature, which was highest at 2 p.m. and lowest at 4 a.m., was superimposed on a steady

general fall of temperature due to other than diurnal
influences—say, the gradual setting in of cold northerly
winds. The line on which the diurnal curve is superimposed
is called the mean level of variation. In the familiar curve
of mean diurnal variation, such as B or C in Fig. 32,
the straight horizontal line A represents the mean
temperature of the place, and the curves B or C are the
resulting traces. If they are unaltered, the only effect of any
change in the level of A would be to bring the whole nearer
or further from the base of the figure. For the level of A
might either be 40° or 70°, but the shape and magnitudes
of the diurnal curves B or C would be the same.

When we come to deal with the significance of a curve
for any particular day, the horizontal line A no longer
represents the mean temperature of the station, but the
level of temperature from general causes independent of
the time of day. If the thermograph gave such a trace
as B or C, it is possible, from geometrical considerations, to
draw the line A, which denotes the level of general
temperature on which the diurnal curves are superposed.
The method is as follows : As B and C are both diurnal
curves which only differ in magnitude, but not in character,
we shall confine our attention to C only. Then, if the
instrumental trace gave C, find from it the mean temperature
of the day by taking the mean of the readings at every hour ;
mark this value m on the vertical hour-line for noon ;
join n and t, the points where the trace cuts the first and
second midnight hour-lines ; then a line A drawn through
m parallel to nt is the level of variation required. The line
nt is omitted in the diagram for the sake of greater clearness.

But now suppose that the diurnal variation B or
C remained the same, but that from other causes the general
temperature fell so uniformly that it may be represented
by a straight line such as D, what would the resulting trace
be like ? This we can easily find graphically by drawing the
line D and taking it as the variable level on which to add
B and C. To do this we have only to measure the values

of B and C at different hours from the level of the line D at the same hour. For instance, the minima at 4 a.m. of E and F are the same distance from D that B and C are from A at the same hour ; also at 8 a.m. and 8 p.m. the diurnal curves equally cross the line of general level, and the maxima at 2 p.m. are also at equal distances from that level. Now look at the resulting curves E and F. The latter, which is the stronger, is able, as it were, to reverse for a few hours the general fall of the line D, and everyone would recognize that there was a diurnal range. Then turn to curve E. Here the diurnal variation is so small that it can only deflect, but not reverse, the general slope of line D. Thus we get the result that the thermometer may fall all day, and yet that there may be a very distinct diurnal variation with its maximum and minimum which, however, serve only to modify the rate of fall of the general slope of the curve.

We have taken our illustration from temperature curves, as their diurnal changes are the simplest and most obvious ; but the same general principles apply to every meteorological element.

In barograms the diurnal variations in Great Britain are so small compared to the general changes that the former can usually be neglected ; but in the tropics, as we see in a later chapter, the pressure as a regular daily event often falls 3 or 4 mb. in six hours, while the general changes of an approaching distant hurricane reach half that amount. In these cases the discrimination between general changes and diurnal variation of pressure is of vital importance.

The question of sorting out various sources of barometric movement is so important in every branch of meteorology that we must give the subject in greater detail.

BAROMETRIC TENDENCY

The manner and rapidity with which the pressure rises or falls is called the " barometric tendency ". This is usually expressed by saying how many hundredths of an inch, or how many millibars, the pressure changes in some fixed period such as an hour or perhaps three hours.

In a variable climate like Great Britain anything under half a millibar per hour is a low rate, while anything over 1½ or 2 millibars may be considered high. On only a few occasions in the year will 4 mb. per hour be exceeded, though as high as twice this quantity has been recorded in exceptional cases. In the tropics diurnal variation alone may give the rate first mentioned above and anything higher than this would be a warning of danger. In connection with the relation of cyclone-motion and gradients to barometric

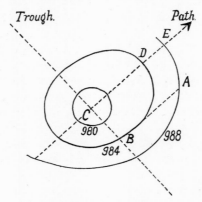

FIG. 33.—Barometric Tendency.

tendency, it may be expedient to give some further explanations. If we look at the diagram of a cyclone given in Fig. 33 it is obvious that the rate of fall of A's barometer will depend on three things—the velocity of the cyclone, the steepness of the gradients, and the position of the observer relative to the cyclone-centre. In published weather charts the isobars are usually drawn for pressure intervals of 4 mb. If we assume that a distance equal to A B would be traversed by the cyclone-centre in four hours, A's rate would be 4 mb. in 4 hours, or 1 mb. per hour, as the distance between the isobars is 4 mb. ; and it is evident that this rate might be doubled by doubling either the velocity of the cyclone or the steepness of the barometric difference between the isobars. Then in the same cyclone, with the same velocity and gradients, the rate to E, who was in the line of the cyclone's path, would be much greater than that to A, who was more remote. In this diagram the distance E D is about half A B, so that E's barometric tendency would be double that of A.

From these considerations we can see that a rapid fall of the barometer indicates danger, because in a general way it shows that the observer is nearly in a line with the path of the cyclone, that the gradients are steep, and that the disturbance is moving rapidly. The first gives an almost complete reversal of the wind, which is most dangerous to ships ; the second high wind ; while the third increases the rapidity of weather changes in every way.

When we come to discuss squalls and thunderstorms we shall find that the pressure often jumps up quite 3 mb. or about 0·1 in. in a few minutes, just as the heavy rain begins. A complex case arises sometimes with the squall in the trough of a cyclone. As the wind goes round with gusts and heavy rain, the pressure turns upwards and rises with a sudden jump. Sometimes a slight fall then occurs, but directly afterwards the barometer rises quickly and steadily. Most of the first jump is due to the squall, and only a very small part to the general increase of pressure due to the passing on of the cyclone.

We have already explained that a barogram is a section, as it were, of a cyclone which is seen in plan on a synoptic chart. This, however, only holds good on the supposition that the cyclone changes neither in depth nor shape during the time which elapses between the beginning and the end of the trace. Now, in practice a cyclone is usually changing both its depth and shape ; and consequently, it is often extremely difficult to see how the changes of pressure which are seen on two synoptic charts at even a short interval would have influenced the trace of the barometer at any one place. Two or more sets of general changes are going on simultaneously, and we have to work out the result of their combination. But the importance of investigating the question will be evident when we remark that on this depend all the apparently anomalous movements of the barometer. If the pressure always fell before rain, and rose when the weather began to mend, meteorology would be simpler ; but we often see rain while the barometer is rising, or the sky begin to clear while pressure is still on the decrease.

Suppose that, as in Fig. 33, a cyclone, with centre at C, was moving along the dotted line marked " path " at such a rate that it would traverse a distance equal to A B in four hours. Then—noting that the isobars at A and B are 4 mb. of pressure apart, that the line A B is parallel to the path of the cyclone, and that B is on the line of the trough, where the barometer naturally begins to rise— if the cyclone moved onwards without any change in the depth of the centre, which is 980 mb., the barometer at station A would fall 4 mb. in these four hours, and then commence to mount.

But now suppose that, while the centre moved onwards, the cyclone began to fill up at the rate of 5 mb. in the four hours (and this is quite within practical limits), then the barometer at A would rise on balance 1 mb. in that time. In fact, it might be supposed to fall 4 mb. from the approach of the cyclone's trough, but to rise 5 mb. from filling up, so that a gain of 1 mb. would remain. Thus we explain the apparent anomaly of the barometer rising while a cyclone approaches ; and here we see the enormous gain to knowledge which synoptic charts have effected. Before the days of synoptic meteorology these barometric anomalies were inexplicable ; now we can interpret them readily, for we know that rain and wind depend on the shape mainly, rather than the level, of the isobars. So that, though the cyclone is filling up and the barometer rising, the wind and weather at station A may sometimes remain characteristic of the front of a cyclone.

SURGE

Any change of barometric level which is not due to the passage of some sort of depression or diurnal variation is called a " surge " of pressure. The expression was introduced by Abercromby to denote this definite and important phenomenon.

We have just explained the idea of a moving cyclone filling up, and of the resulting balance of a gain of pressure. It would have been just as easy for the cyclone to grow deeper in the same time, when we should have had the barometer falling in rear of the cyclone, with clearing weather. Sometimes filling up of a cyclone is tolerably local ; at other times surging is on an enormous scale. Nothing is more common in winter than to find a moderate sized cyclone in mid-Atlantic one day, and that though by next morning the shape of the isobars has hardly changed, the whole level of pressure in the cyclone and surroundings has decreased appreciably.

This hardly shows at first on a synoptic chart, for one sees no change in the configuration of the lines ; but on looking at the figures attached to the isobars which denote the level, one sees that what was 1,000 mb. the first day is perhaps only 990 mb. on the following morning. In like manner a persistent anticyclone will often rise and fall a few millibars without any motion or material change of shape on the chart, while the barometer at any station will have appeared to rise or fall without any reason or apparent change of weather.

When we look at a series of these surges we find a decided tendency of the motion to travel from west to east, or from south-west to north-east. For instance, suppose that one day there was a deep depression with one or more cyclones in the United States, an anticyclone in mid-Atlantic, and a shallow set of depressions over Europe. We might find by next morning that the American cyclones were filling up and that the Atlantic high pressure was lower in level but unchanged in position, while the European system was practically unaltered. The third day might see that, with little change in America, the Atlantic anticyclone had regained its former level, while a great decrease of pressure had occurred over the whole of Europe.

A surge of itself has no characteristic weather, but the passage of a surge exercises a moderate influence on the characteristic weather of any isobaric shape, and a very powerful one on the formation of new systems.

Let us define the front of a surge as all the part where pressure is decreasing, the rear as all the part where pressure is increasing, the trough as the line of change from fall to rise, and the crest as the line of change from rise to fall. Then we find that the front of a moving surge, or the mere deepening of a cyclone, does not alter the typical character of the front and rear of the cyclone, but increases the general intensity ; while the rising part of a surge decreases the intensity and so improves the weather. The lowering of an anticyclone decreases the dryness and increases the tendency to form cloud, while a gain of pressure has the opposite effect. But the most striking and by far the most important effect of surge is the influence on the development of new systems of disturbance. The tendency of all reduction of barometric level all over the world is to induce cyclonic systems, while that of gain of pressure is to dissipate existing cyclones.

We shall find abundant examples of this great principle in our illustrations of types of temperate weather. There, as we have just mentioned, surge and cyclone are so mixed up together that we can only partially disentangle them ; but in the tropics we find the same law under simpler conditions. For instance, in the south Indian Ocean, during the period of the north-west monsoon—from about December to March—there is a long furrow of low pressure in about 10° south latitude, where the north-west monsoon meets the south-east trade. During the whole of that season this general depression goes through a series of small surges, gradually lowering, perhaps one-tenth of an inch (3 mb.) for six or seven days, and then rising about the same amount in another week. Now, as a matter of observation, hurricanes almost invariably form during the downward period of the surge, and practical forecasters are always specially on the look-out for signs of serious bad weather whenever there is the slightest symptom of a non-diurnal diminution of pressure.

ISALLOBARIC CHARTS

If we plot the barometric tendencies reported from all the observing stations on the synoptic chart and—after the manner of drawing isobars—draw instead lines connecting up all the places showing equal changes of pressure, we get what is known as a chart of isallobars. In practice the changes are generally reported in the form of the rise or fall of pressure in the three hours preceding the time of observation. The isallobars give us a bird's-eye view of the areas of rising pressure and the areas of falling pressure, as well as the extent of the changes. In considering successive charts it is found that the isallobaric configurations drift across the map in a manner that resembles the movement of anticyclones or cyclones. The possible practical uses of isallobaric charts have been explored by Nils Ekholm and E. G. Bilham, the latter of whom stated his conclusions in the following terms : " When the pressure distribution is accurately known both at the beginning and end of the time interval, the point at issue is whether the isallobaric chart is capable of affording any additional information, or of displaying the available information in a more effective way. We have found in the case of small depressions uncomplicated by other systems that the isallobars are merely a sort of composite picture of the two sets of isobars and no additional information is imparted by them. The same is true of large depressions. In most cases we found, in fact, that the isallobars tended to be more complex than the pressures distributions giving rise to them. No additional information as to the course taken by the depression in moving from its initial to its final position is afforded by the isallobaric chart since, as has previously been pointed out, the isallobars depend only on the initial and final conditions, and not on intermediate stages.

" When the distribution is complex, however, the isallobaric chart is of value since it performs the function of separating the active from the quiescent features of the pressure distribution. Since complexity is the normal condition of isobaric charts, any method whereby certain outstanding features could be disentangled from their surroundings would seem to be worthy of attention. An isallobaric chart is clearly capable of presenting to the eye a picture of the state of affairs which would not be readily perceived on the ordinary chart."

The physical significance of the isallobars in certain cases has been examined more recently by D. Brunt and C. K. M. Douglas. Their investigation relates primarily to cases where, in consequence of a changing pressure distribution, the wind—even at a height of 600 metres above ground—has not acquired a constant speed and come into balance with the pressure gradient. They show how an estimate of the deviation of the actual wind from the geostrophic wind can be derived from an isallobaric chart ; also they attribute the occurrence of rain in isallobaric lows and of fine weather in isallobaric highs to the effects of con-vergence (leading to general upward motion of air) or divergence (leading to general downward motion) respectively over the regions of deviation.

BIBLIOGRAPHY

Practical Examples of Polar Front Analysis over the British Isles in 1925-6. J. Bjerknes. London : Meteorological Office Geoph. Mem., No. 50 (1930). Price 3s.
The Modification of the Strophic Balance for Changing Pressure Distribution and its Effect on Rainfall. D. Brunt and C. K. M. Douglas. Roy. Met. Soc. Mem., vol. iii, No. 22 (1928).

Chapter VII

WIND AND CALM

The Relation to Barometric Pressure

In a previous chapter we have indicated the empirical law that in most cases the velocity of the wind is roughly proportional to the closeness of the isobars ; the relative closeness of any two isobars is known as the barometric gradient, being measured by the steepness of the barometric slope which they indicate. In the same way as on an orographical map with contour lines one measures the steepness of the gradients of hills and valleys by considering the rate at which the elevation varies along the normal or shortest line between two contours, so in the meteorological problem the barometric gradient is defined as the rate of fall or pressure along the direction of steepest slope. In practical synoptic meteorology special scales are employed, which when laid across the isobars so as to measure the perpendicular distance between successive isobars, enable one to read off at once the speed of the " gradient wind ". The theory according to which these scales are computed is given below. The law of the relation between wind and the distribution of barometric pressure was first enunciated as an empirical one by Professor Buys Ballot, of Utrecht, in 1857, and only later has it received a dynamical explanation.

In this explanation the rotation of the earth has to be taken into account. If any body is set in motion and left to itself it will tend to describe a straight path in space and thus its motion over any small portion of the earth's surface would not appear as a straight line, because the earth all the time is rotating under the moving body. It is for this reason that a rifle bullet deviates to the right in the northern hemisphere and to the left in the southern hemisphere. For the same reason the right banks of rivers (in the northern hemisphere) tend to be more worn by the action of the current than the left banks ; a right to left force must, in fact, be applied if the moving body is to be kept moving in the same direction relatively to the earth's surface. In books on dynamics it is shown that the force required is given by $2\rho V\omega \sin \phi$, where ρ is the mass of the body, V its velocity, ω the angular velocity of the earth, and ϕ the latitude. In the atmosphere the air is subjected continually to a force b say, due to the pressure gradient and tending to push the air from high pressure towards low, and if this force just balances that required by the earth's rotation the air will be kept moving along the isobars. Thus with air moving along straight isobars and with uniform speed we have the equation—

$$b = 2\rho V\omega \sin \phi$$

Generally, however, the air is not moving exactly in a straight path, but in a slightly curved one, so that a further term has to be added to the equation to allow for centrifugal action. The centrifugal tendency is proportional to the square of the velocity divided by the radius of curvature of the path of the air mass, i.e. if r is the radius of the path described by the mass of air the term due to centrifugal action is $\dfrac{\rho V^2}{r}$. For the cyclonic sense of motion this term acts in the same direction as the term arising from the deflecting force due to the earth's rotation ; so that the complete equation for air moving in a curved path becomes

$$\frac{b}{\rho} = 2V\omega \sin \phi + \frac{V^2}{r}$$

The two terms on the right-hand side of the equation are known as the geostrophic and the cyclostrophic terms respectively. For motion in the anticyclonic sense the second term becomes negative.

A more elaborate analysis of weather maps is required

to determine the curvature of the actual path of the air
(and except in tropical revolving storms the curvature is
not usually great), but the fundamental principle is that the
force arising from the pressure gradient is balanced by
appropriate action of the air.

What we have just said applies to what is called the free
air, that is the air at some little distance above the earth's
surface.   Air near the ground is retarded in its movements
by friction with the ground ; the effect is, in fact, so great
that any mass of air that remained in contact with the ground
would very soon be brought to rest. The effect of turbulence
(which has already been mentioned in connection with the
variation of temperature with height) is, however, to cause
a certain degree of mixing of air at different levels.   Thus
masses of air from the ground go up to greater heights,
and other masses from those greater heights where the air
is moving freely under the influence of the pressure gradient
are continually being brought down to ground level, bringing
with them their contribution of forward momentum.   Thus,
depending on the degree of turbulence, there is interchange
of momentum between different atmospheric layers, and the
surface layers are dragged on, though at a speed less than
that of the upper layers. The direction of the surface layers
is also affected. Whenever the air is retarded, as by ground
friction, and reduced to a speed lower than that of balance
with the barometric gradient, the gradient has some effect
in pushing the air across the isobars towards the direction
of lower pressure.   In consequence of this, the surface
wind, as well as being retarded in speed, ordinarily blows
at an angle to the isobars and not exactly along them.

The idea of the balance between wind speed and pressure
gradient may perhaps be made clearer by analogy with
what happens on a curved racing track for motor-cars.
A track of this sort is built with the camber of the road
surface increasing gradually from the inner edge to the
outer edge of the track, so that drivers may select a camber
of steepness appropriate to the curvature of the track and
the speed at which they wish to travel. If the speed of a car

is too high for the camber or transverse gradient of the track at the place where the car is travelling the car will tend to run towards the outer edge ; if the speed is too low the tendency will be to run down towards the inner edge. It is the same with the air when under the control of the barometric pressure gradient. We may think of the isobars as contours on the racing track ; if the air speed is too low the air is pushed inwards towards the low pressure and travels at an angle with the isobars.

Variation of Wind with Height

It is found that at a height of some 1,500 or 2,000 feet above ground and under average conditions the wind approximates closely to the theoretical gradient value both in speed and in direction. The manner in which the wind changes as we proceed from that height down to the ground varies very greatly, depending, as we have said above, on how far the accessions of momentum carried down by turbulent movements can compete with the retardations caused by the ground. Consequently, at night, when there is little convectional turbulence the wind at ground level frequently dies away. In the daytime, again, it freshens up. This question is gone into more fully in the chapter on diurnal variations.

At heights above a kilometre or two the influence of surface effects and surface turbulence may almost be disregarded, and the changes of wind speed and direction which we find at various levels are for the most part associated with corresponding changes in the barometric gradient. Sometimes, for example, an easterly wind at lower levels decreases in speed with increasing height, and finally gives place to a westerly wind ; quite often, indeed, the westerly component of a wind gradually increases with height.

For an explanation of such phenomena we must consider how the distribution of pressure across our synoptic chart is itself likely to change with height ; in other words, how much pressure is to be deducted at one place as compared with another when we raise our level of reference and try to picture the isobars at, say, three kilometres. A common condition, for example, in our latitudes is that temperature falls gradually from south to north. On this account the first three kilometres of air above, say, Edinburgh, being colder than those over London, will have greater mass than the corresponding three kilometres of air above London ; and in such a case the pressure must diminish more rapidly from London to Edinburgh at a height of three kilometres than it does at ground level. In other words, the westerly component of the gradient wind in such a case is greater at a height of three kilometres than it is at ground level.[1]

THE SOUTHERN HEMISPHERE

So far we have dealt with winds in the northern hemisphere. It is easy to follow the modifications which occur south of the Equator. The general principles are the same, but what does differ is that portion of Buys Ballot's law which gives the direction of the wind in relation to the low or high pressure. For the southern hemisphere the low pressure is on one's right when one stands with one's back to the wind ; that is to say, the wind in a cyclone rotates in clockwise direction, in an anticyclone in counter-clockwise direction.

AVERAGE FLOW OF AIR

From what has been said the reader will have realized that a chart with isobars has an interest and a value, not simply as a picture of the distribution of atmospheric pressure, but as a representation of the flow of air at the time to which the chart relates. And further, if an isobaric chart be constructed from the mean pressure readings of a month,

---

[1] The general problem involves pressure change as well as temperature change. The formula for the rate of increase of pressure difference, in mb. per metre increase of height is $\cdot 0342 \frac{p}{\theta}\left(\frac{\Delta\theta}{\theta}-\frac{\Delta p}{p}\right)$ where p, θ denote pressure and temperature and $\Delta p, \Delta \theta$ the differences in the horizontal direction.

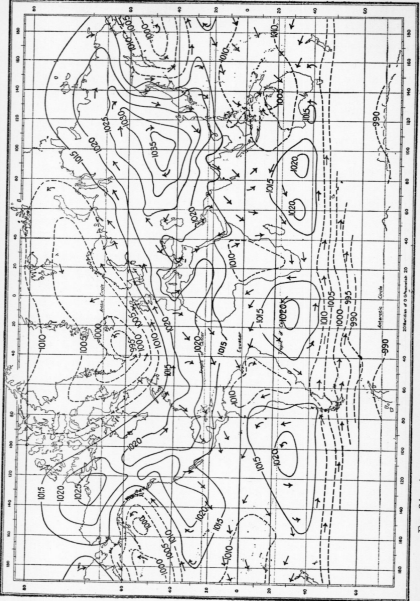

FIG. 34.—Average pressure at mean sea level and prevailing winds at the surface in January.

Fig. 35.—Average pressure at mean sea level and prevailing winds at the surface in July.

season, or year, the chart may similarly be regarded as giving the resultant drift of air for the period in question. Fig. 34 gives the average pressure at mean sea level and the prevailing winds over the surface of the globe in January. There it will be seen that under average conditions pressure is low in the North Atlantic between Iceland and Greenland and high in the region of the Azores. Associated with this pressure distribution a great south-westerly current blows from the Atlantic across the British Isles and Norway. Without this warm, moist current the winter climate of our latitude would be relatively severe. On the contrary, Eastern Canada and the United States are subjected to a north-westerly current from Arctic regions and their winter climate in consequence is dry and very cold.

Fig. 35 shows that in summer the average air current over the British Isles is more nearly westerly and considerably reduced in speed.

CALMS

Calms, if not purely surface ones, are the product of no barometric gradient. The most persistent calms are found in the " doldrums ", or the col of low pressure near the Equator between the north-east and south-east trade winds all over the world.

In temperate regions the most persistent calms are near the centres of stationary anticyclones ; but more short-lived calms are found in the centres of cyclones, along the crest of wedges, and in cols.

WIND PRESSURE

We may say a few words here about the relation of force to velocity. The velocity is a definite quantity but the force exerted by the wind on an obstacle depends largely on the shape of the obstacle. According to the theory of stream-lines, whenever a fluid meets an obstacle, if the angles of the obstacle do not break the continuity of the fluid so as to form eddies or vortices, the same amount of pressure which is imposed on the body by the first deflection of the fluid is given back again as the stream-lines of the fluid close up behind the obstruction. For instance, if a ship is lying at anchor in a current, the same amount of strain which the current causes on her cable when the water is forced asunder by the bows is given back when the current closes in behind her ; so that the total pressure which she experiences is only that due to the friction of the water on her skin. This is, of course, on the supposition that her lines are so easy that they do not break the stream-lines so as to form little eddies or vortices.

Now, the same thing holds with wind. If we put up two square plates of different sizes, face to the wind, the pressure on each is not exactly proportional to the area, while in light breezes neither may record anything. The reason is that in light wind a thin mobile fluid like air can glide round even the sharp angles of a square without forming eddies, and as there is no vacuum formed behind the plate there is no pressure recorded. In higher winds the stream-lines are broken, and every shape and every sized plate of the same shape form a different series of eddies round the rim of the obstacle.

From this it follows that, though we might say that the pressure on a board 1 foot square was 20 lb., and might compare this force with that on another board of the same size and mounting, we should scarcely be justified in saying that the force of the wind was 20 lb. per square foot in the abstract, because a board 10 feet square, even if of the same shape, would have given a slightly different number.

If all the other things are equal, however, the pressure exerted by the wind on a flat surface is proportional to the area and to the square of the wind speed. The formulæ connecting the wind pressure (P) with the speed (V) and the Beaufort Force (B) are—

$$P = \cdot 003 \ V^2$$
$$\text{and } P = \cdot 0105 \ B^3$$

where P is expressed in pounds per square foot and V in miles per hour.

WIND STRUCTURE

We may include in this section a few remarks on wind structure. The wind is never entirely steady, but fluctuates continually in speed and direction. In nature the nearest approach to a steady wind is one in which the variations are regular and small compared with the mean wind speed. Anemographs have been devised to give a complete record of wind speed and direction with all their momentary variations, and Fig. 31 contains an example of a record of this sort from a Dines pressure tube anemograph. These brief variations of wind speed and direction are of two main classes, known technically as gustiness and squalliness. The first comprises the more momentary fluctuations, which take place in periods of a few seconds and which cause the anemogram to appear as a " ribbon " rather than as a line. They are the result of turbulence in the air, arising in part from the convectional eddies to which we have already referred as existing always in the troposphere and more markedly near the ground, and in part from frictional eddies induced in the air as it passes over the land or sea surface.

So long as the " ribbon " appears as one of sensibly constant width laid evenly on the chart, it signifies gustiness, but no squalliness. The latter property is indicated by waves, kinks, and other irregularities in the ribbon ; that is, it is associated with wind fluctuations which take anything from some minutes up to perhaps two hours to develop and pass away. Squalliness probably arises sometimes from a wave effect between overlying layers of atmosphere of appreciably different speeds or directions. In these cases fairly regular waves are indicated on the anemogram. At other times the anemogram has a saw-toothed appearance, with the rises in speed sharp and the falls in speed gradual. This latter type is considered to be associated with instability in the atmosphere leading to a quasi-periodic overturning of the masses of atmosphere as they move along.   In this scheme the steep rises of wind speed are associated with accessions of momentum from masses of air freshly descended from higher levels.

In the anemogram of Fig. 31 the part between 2 h. and 6 h. affords an example of a wind of a considerable range of gustiness, i.e. a broad " ribbon ", without squalliness. On the other hand, the part between 20 h. and 22 h., though not a good example, shows squalliness of a wave type, which is rather characteristic of the wind in this part of the front of an advancing depression. The part between 6 h. and 9 h. shows squalliness of rather a different type, probably associated with instability, the rises of speed being rapid and the falls of speed more gradual, and again rather characteristic of the newly arrived cold air in the region of the squall line.

LAND AND SEA BREEZES

Land and sea breezes are experienced on coasts in fine summer weather. In a later chapter we explain that during the day the air over the land rises much more in temperature than does the air over the sea. Let us consider the effect on a stratum of air which at sunrise, let us say, lay 1,000 feet thick over both land and sea. As the forenoon rise of temperature proceeds, this stratum obviously must bulge up more over the land than over the sea. Some of the air higher up will then tend to run off down the slope towards the sea until a state of equilibrium is reached. This slight transfer of air from land to sea at the higher levels, however, causes the pressure at sea at all lower levels to correspondingly exceed that over the land at the same levels, and so the surface air is impelled to move as a sea breeze from sea to land. During the night the conditions are reversed, and we find a land breeze blowing out to sea. These land and sea breezes are quite shallow and quite local to the coast-line, seldom reaching a height of more than 1,000 feet or penetrating beyond about 10 to 15 miles on either side of the coast-line. The sea breeze is the more marked part of the phenomenon.

KATABATIC AND ANABATIC WINDS

Another kind of local wind, which is frequently diurnal in its incidence, is the wind known as " katabatic ". This is the name given to the gravitation of cold air off high ground, and such a wind can also be much more than a mere diurnal effect. At nights, however, in clear settled weather breezes originate in this way. The air in contact with mountain slopes is cooled at night more quickly than the free air at the same horizontal level over the valleys ; the heavier chilled air flows down the slopes towards the bottoms of the valleys, and is continually replaced by warmer air coming in from the free atmosphere at about the same level but overlying the valleys. The cool downward breeze is known as a katabatic wind. The opposite kind of wind, a current up the mountain sides during the day, is sometimes called an anabatic wind. Regarding cases of katabatic winds that are more than mere diurnal effects we may quote a note from the Barometer Manual for the Use of Seamen :—

" With high plateaux and steep slopes a very violent wind is sometimes caused by the air cooled on the plateaux running over the edges and down the slopes as a cataract of cold air. This is notably the case on the Eastern and Western Coasts of Greenland and probably the winds of the western part of the ice barrier of the Ross Sea in the Antarctic are cataract winds of like character. Probably the blizzards experienced by Sir Douglas Mawson's expedition owed their origin to that cause, as there is no limit to the violence of the wind if the air is sufficiently cooled before or during the descent. It may be allowed that the air gains in temperature by one degree for every 190 feet of drop, and that the rise of temperature will diminish the density of the falling air. That will diminish and may stop the flow, but if the air is sufficiently chilled to start with and gets further chilled by a cold surface on the way, very violent winds may be produced. . . . The setting up of a katabatic wind may be partly dependent upon the distribution of pressure because a particular distribution may set up a circulation under which the katabatic conditions are developed, but the ultimate strength of it is not determined by the pressure distribution. . . .

" It is not improbable that the katabatic winds of the polar regions and the ice-covered slopes of the Northern and Southern continents may be a primary factor in maintaining the circulation of the atmosphere. The one surface or the other is exposed to the sky during the long polar night, and there must be in consequence a constant katabatic stream of air flowing from the highlands to the plains and to sea-level and running off the land like water."

REGIONAL WINDS

In many countries there occur from time to time winds of so marked characteristics as to have earned special names. From the physical point of view these winds are not all different, but rather belong to certain main groups and it will be convenient here to discuss them according to these groups.

Scirocco, Khamsin

When a depression passes from west to east along the Mediterranean, the southerly or south-easterly wind in front of it comes off the African coast as a very hot, dry wind. In crossing the Mediterranean this wind becomes heavily charged with water vapour, so that it reaches Malta and Italy and other parts of southern Europe as a wind not only hot but unpleasantly humid ; this wind is known as the scirocco.

Under similar meteorological conditions, that is, with a depression passing eastward along the Mediterranean, the southerly wind experienced over Egypt is known as the khamsin, but as it has come from the interior of a tropical continent and has not passed over any sea it remains hot and dry.

Föhn, Chinook

The warm dry winds which quite frequently blow down the northern slopes of the Alps are known locally as the Föhn, and the similar type of wind occurring on the eastern side of the Rocky Mountains is there called the Chinook. Similar winds occur rather less frequently on the southern side of the Alps and occur also on the coast of Greenland and in many other mountainous districts ; but it is in the Swiss valleys that the Föhn is best known, and the circumstances which lead to its occurrence there will now be described. When a fairly extensive depression is centred over North-West Europe the south wind in its front may cross the Alps. On arrival at the south side of the mountains this wind is warm and moist, so that it does not require to rise far before the cooling causes condensation to commence. The subsequent rise, as we have explained in the chapter on the Upper Air, is attended by cooling only at the saturated adiabatic rate, that is, at the rate of about 3° F per 1,000 feet, and during this time the formation of cloud proceeds continuously. With an ascent sufficiently prolonged heavy rain occurs. After reaching the top the descent on the other side begins, so that instead of adiabatic cooling the air now undergoes adiabatic warming. At the beginning the air may require to descend a few hundred feet before the cloud carried over in it has evaporated. During the remainder of the descent the warming, however, is at the dry adiabatic rate, i.e. at the rate of 5·4° F per 1000 feet. Thus, if the air on the south side of the mountains rose, let us say, 6,000 feet after saturation had been attained, it would drop in temperature during that time by some 18°, and if on the north side it descended again through a similar height it would rise in temperature by some 32°, a net gain in temperature of 14°. This rise of temperature, it will be seen, has been achieved at the loss of all the moisture shed as rain in the course of the ascent and the heat gained has been derived from the "latent heat" given up when the moisture condensed. A typical case in winter would be where the air would arrive at the foot-hills on the south side of the Alps with a temperature of 65° F and practically saturated with moisture ; that is, its dew-point would also be about 65°. It might have to rise a further 9,000 feet and then descend perhaps 6,000 feet before reaching the high valleys on the north side of the Alps. Thus its temperature would first fall about 27°, i.e. to 38°, and afterwards rise some 30° (allowing 2° for loss of heat in various ways, as by contact with cold ground), so that finally its temperature would be about 68°, whilst its dew-point would only be 38° (or perhaps a little higher), so that in these high valleys it would appear as a hot and very dry wind.

When a föhn wind begins to set in there are generally some considerable oscillations of temperature which go on for several hours until all the cold air formerly lying in the high valleys has been stirred up and persuaded to move on somewhere else. The föhn may last for some days at a time.

Bora, Mistral

The bora is the name given to a cold north-easterly wind occasionally experienced in winter in northern Italy and the Adriatic. It is a flood of polar air from the higher parts of Central Europe, and in cases where low temperature and high pressure over Central Europe coincide with the passage of a depression along the Mediterranean the bora in the rear of the depression may attain gale force. In Italy the weather may be either clear—the bora chiara—or dull and gloomy with occasional snow showers—the bora scura.

K

The similar wind, but usually northerly or north-westerly in direction, which occurs on the Mediterranean coast of France, is known as the mistral. It is usually accompanied by bright, clear weather.

Though these winds are partly katabatic in origin, the initial temperature of the air is so much lower than the normal temperature in Mediterranean regions that in spite of some warming in descending from the high ground they reach sea level as relatively cold winds.

Pamperos, Southerly Bursters

These phenomena are merely mentioned here as being accompanied by noteworthy local winds. As they are more, however, of the nature of line squalls of thunderstorm type their description is postponed to the appropriate chapter.

BIBLIOGRAPHY

The Structure of the Atmosphere in Clear Weather. C. J. P. Cave.
Barometric Gradient and Wind Force. E. Gold. London: Meteorological Office Mem., No. 3.
Manual of Meteorology, vol. iv. Sir Napier Shaw. Camb. Univ. Press.
Wind Structure. A. H. R. Goldie. *Royal Air Force Quarterly*, vol. i, No. 1, pp. 107–116.
The Structure of Wind over Level Country. M. A. Giblett and others. London: Meteorological Office Geoph. Mem., No. 54 (1932).

Chapter VIII

HEAT AND COLD

General Control of Temperature

In this chapter we propose to go a little more into the details of the manner in which changes of temperature are produced. What are the causes of burning heat at one time and hard frosts at another time in the same place ; why is the same day of the month hot in one year and cold in another ; why at the same season do hot and cold days follow one another without any apparent sequence ; and why is England sometimes warmer than France, though the latter is nearer the Equator ; or colder than Iceland near the Arctic Circle ?

Briefly we may answer these questions by saying that the anomalies result from the circulation of the air, and that they would not occur if the air did not move up and down and about over the earth, but the explanation of this in detail is necessarily rather a long process.

First we lay down the proposition that if the temperature of the air at a given place changes, the change is the result of one or more of the following possible causes :—

1. Contribution of heat to or abstraction of heat from the air by radiation, convection, condensation, etc.

2. Adiabatic change due to change of pressure.

3. Change due to introduction—which might be either horizontally or vertically—of air of different temperature from neighbouring regions.

The first cause mentioned signifies " home-brewing " of the heat or cold ; the third signifies " importation " ; and the second cause is one which operates as a rule in the course of the " importation ".

DIURNAL ISOTHERMS ON A UNIFORM EARTH

The first of these three possible causes will now be discussed. The sun is the principal source of all heat, and so far as his radiation is concerned the amount available to each unit of the earth's surface varies only according to latitude and season.

As indicating the extent of these variations we give below a table computed by Angot showing the relative amounts of insolation received each day in various latitudes and at various seasons of the year. (The unit used is kilowatt-hours per square dekametre of the earth's surface, with the " solar constant " assumed to be 135 kilowatts per square dekametre.)

TABLE IV

INSOLATION RECEIVED PER DAY

	Equator	20°	40°	60°	90° N.	90° S.
22nd March .	1,038	980	805	532	30	0
21st June .	915	1,085	1,150	1,135	1,249	0
20th September .	1,023	972	805	541	20	0
20th December .	977	702	371	58	0	1,331

The atmosphere, of course, cuts down the amount reaching the earth, and more especially in polar regions, owing to the longer path near the poles.

If nothing caused a variation in the absorption of the solar radiation and if the air did not move about, there would be a regular diminution of temperature from the Equator to the Pole, which we shall call a thermal slope. Moreover, every day, as the earth turned under the sun, a well-defined wave of variation would be imposed on this slope. The lines which mark out this deflected slope we shall call diurnal isotherms. We have first to consider what the shape of the lines would be at any moment over the globe.

The diagram in Fig. 36 is intended to give the ideal shape of the isotherms at any moment. Noon is placed in the middle of the diagram in longitude 180°, and the lines represent the diurnal variation in the latitude of each isotherm.

The scale on the right of the diagram is degrees of latitude ;
that on the left, degrees of temperature. For an ideal
diagram we have supposed that the general slope from the
Equator is 1° of temperature for 1° of latitude. The principle
on which the diagram is formed is as follows : Suppose that
in latitude 20° N. the temperature is 60° F at midnight,
and that by 6 a.m. the temperature has fallen to 59° ;
then we should have to go 1° of latitude further south at
that hour, if we want to follow the position of the isotherm

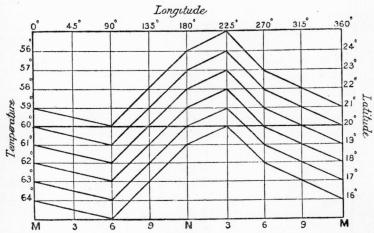

Fig. 36.—Diagram illustrating the shape of diurnal isotherms.

of 60°. If, in our undisturbed world, we could move round
the earth in any latitude in 24 hours, the line marked 60°
on the chart represents what our journey would be if we
wanted to keep under a uniform temperature of 60° for the
whole day. Starting at midnight on the left of the diagram,
we should have to go 60 geographical miles south and 90°
east of longitude by 6 o'clock in the morning. Between then
and 3 p.m. we should have to make 300 miles of northing
and 155° of easting if we still wished to keep our thermometer
at 60° ; and from then till the second midnight we should

have to make 240 miles of southing and 135° of easting
to follow the isotherm of 60°. Observe that the easting has
to be expressed in degrees of longitude, for the number of
miles in a degree varies with the latitude. The diagram is
also based on the supposition that there is a pretty uniform
isothermal slope from the Equator to the Pole, and that the
diurnal range of temperature does not vary much within
5° or 10° of latitude.

Then, if there were no irregularities caused by air movement or the unequal heating of land or water, the diurnal
thermogram in every place would be very similar in shape
to the trace of any of the isotherms as plotted on a chart
if we turn longitude into time, and latitude into degrees of
temperature on a suitable scale. In fact, we may conceive
the curves shown in the diagram to sweep round the world
with the earth's rotation, and suppose that the rise or fall
of temperature at any station was caused by the passage
of this shape of isotherms, just as the motion of the barometer
is the product of the propagation of different shapes of
isobars over any place. For instance, in the diagram
(Fig. 36) the strong horizontal line shows the position of the
section across the diurnal isotherms which is propagated
over any station in lat. 20° north. Starting from the first
midnight on the left of the diagram the thermometer would
mark 60°. By 6 a.m. the temperature would have fallen to
59°, as that isotherm descends to latitude 20° at that hour.
Between 6 a.m. and 3 p.m. five isotherms are propagated
over the station, so that the instrument would register
64° at the latter hour. Then, as lower isotherms begin to
pass over the observer, the temperature would fall at the
rate shown in the figure, till 60° was reached again by the
second midnight.

The ideal conditions described above, then, are such as
we might expect to find if the sun's daily radiation and the
corresponding loss of heat at night took place without
interferences other than those arising from local convection,
evaporation, and condensation.

EFFECT OF LAND OR SEA SURFACE

In the chapter on the Upper Air we have explained that, after traversing the atmosphere, about half of the solar radiation arriving from the sun remains to be absorbed by the earth. Again, in the chapter on Diurnal Variation, under the heading of Diurnal Processes we shall go more fully into the manner and degree in which the heat thus received is used to warm the atmosphere from below. Here, however, we are concerned with the effect of the nature of the surface, land or water, and from our present point of view land and water differ in three important ways. In the first place they have different powers of radiating and absorbing heat. The land is opaque to all radiation, so that the solar radiation is stopped at the very surface and converted into heat. Thus the whole of the heat absorbed by the land surface goes towards raising the temperature of a very thin layer of earth, and therefore the surface temperature rises rapidly and very greatly. Water, on the other hand, is comparatively transparent to the heat rays, so that some of the radiation penetrates to an appreciable depth and in this way the heat is distributed throughout a considerable body of water ; the water therefore rises little in temperature as compared with the land.

In the second place land and water differ in regard to their " specific heats " in such a way that a much greater amount of heat is needed to raise a mass of water by a given number of degrees than is needed to raise the same weight of land. Thus on this account also, if the same amount of solar radiation were available to both, the land would rise more considerably in temperature than would the water.

In the third place comes the most important question of mobility. The continual movement both horizontally and vertically and the consequent mixing which go on in the sea enable any heat received at the surface to be rapidly dispersed throughout a large body of water. The land has no method of distributing the superficially received heat, other than the rather slow one of conduction.

As a result of these different powers of absorbing, of storing, and of distributing heat, and of the different power of radiating to which we shall refer in a moment, we have on the part of the oceans a great conservatism and on the part of the land areas a great liability to rapid changes in the matter of temperature. The deep oceans act like great reservoirs of heat or cold, maintaining a much more even temperature throughout the year and between day and night than the continental areas. Because of their incapacity for storing or distributing heat, the continents become superficially hotter in summer and colder in winter, hotter by day and colder by night. We shall refer to this matter again in connection with the question of diurnal variations.

We have so far been considering chiefly the results accruing from the incoming solar radiation. The principal cause of loss of heat is outward radiation into space, and here again the land areas lose more rapidly and for the reasons outlined above they can lose but little heat without a considerable drop in temperature, having little reserve to draw upon. Bodies on the earth's surface which radiate away heat at night chill the air in contact with them ; the air also radiates away heat, but is not a very good radiator.

A striking result of this is that on a calm, clear night the air close to the ground may become much colder than the air at some little height in the atmosphere ; and on such nights inversions of temperature at low levels over land areas are quite common.

The conditions conducive to such a result are a still air, a clear sky, and paucity of water vapour in any stratum of the atmosphere. The last condition is important, because, as we have mentioned in the chapter on the Upper Air, water vapour is a great absorber of radiation, so that when much water vapour is present it has a blanketing effect and the ground cannot lose its heat so rapidly as when the air is dry. The first condition, a still air, is important also because in the absence of wind there is nothing to cause the air after it has been cooled near the ground to mix with the warmer and lighter air at higher levels. Pretty much the same air thus remains near the ground and becomes colder and colder as the night advances.

All the conditions for great and lasting surface cold are fulfilled in the most perfect manner in Siberia in winter. In that high latitude the winter sun has little power, and in the centre of a vast continental area we start usually with calm and relative dryness. Even if the air were not calm to begin with, the surface air, as it became cold and dense, would gradually separate out from the upper wind circulation and fall calm. Thus in winter the continent becomes covered with a layer of cold air which ever becomes colder.

The effect of the contraction of this lower layer of atmosphere is to induce inflow of air at higher levels from surrounding areas so that additional air gradually accumulates over the whole continent ; in other words, an intense anticyclone is formed. Indeed, in Siberia there have been recorded in winter some of the highest pressures—as high as 1,071 mb.—and the lowest surface temperatures—as low as — 93° F—of the globe. This region, then, is a great reservoir of cold air in winter.

Starting with the idea of the different capacities of land and sea for storing heat, Otto Myrbach developed a theory known as the " Breathing of the Continents ". Owing to the differences we have outlined, a continent warms and cools more rapidly and to a greater extent than the oceans. The winter process of accumulation of air to which we have just referred in the case of Siberia is described by Myrbach as the continent breathing in. The reverse process, the break-up of these winter continental anticyclones, is called by Myrbach the continent breathing out. This breathing of the continents is a useful way of describing seasonal phenomena which, as we shall see in later chapters, have an important bearing on weather and weather types and an important disturbing effect on the pressure distribution and the general circulation of the atmosphere over the globe. Reference to the World Isobars in Figs. 34 and 35 of Chapter VII will show how marked is the tendency for high pressure to form over continental areas in winter and over the oceans in summer, whilst low pressures lie over the continents in summer and over the oceans in winter.

From what has been said in this section it will be seen that geographical conditions in themselves introduce a great complication into the regular system of isotherms, which we considered in the previous section of this chapter as appropriate to an ideally uniform earth. We may sum up the complication in so far as temperature is concerned by saying that over every continental area we have in summer a supply of air much warmer than the average for the latitude, and in winter a supply of air much colder than the average for the latitude, whilst over the oceans we have air which is cooler in summer and warmer in winter than for its latitude as a whole. Thus whereas on a uniform globe we should look to the southward for warm air and to the northward for cold air, we have in actual practice to take into account the superposed effect of geographical conditions. We may now consider that we have dealt with control of temperature on the spot, i.e. with what we called " home-brewing " of temperature. Next, starting from this point, we turn to the possibilities in the way of " importation ".

Movement of Air

We quote a note from the *Barometer Manual for the Use of Seamen* :—

" Of the millions of tons of air which form the atmosphere nearly the whole is moving. The regions of calm at the surface at any one time taken all together do not form a large part of the earth's surface, and above the surface calm regions are still rarer. Let us remember that the motion of the air is always " circulation " ; air cannot move forward or backward or upward or downward without

displacing other air in front of it and being replaced by other
air behind it. The circulation may be quite local and limited
in extent, as is frequently the case when warm air rises or
cold air sinks. In the course of investigations into the life
history of surface air currents in the Meteorological Office
we have traced air over long stretches of the surface of the
Atlantic. We have found on one occasion the shores of
Greenland to be fed with air that left the middle of the
Atlantic four days previously, while in the course of six
days air travelled from Spitzbergen to join the North-East
Trade Wind off the West Coast of Africa. On another
occasion the air that formed the wind off the South of
Ireland was traced back to the North of Africa, but that
which blew at the opening of the Channel two days later
came from Hudson's Bay, via the Azores. These long
journeys were performed in a way that is in striking
resemblance to the passage of a fast ship."

Therefore, when we come to forecast the temperature on
any day in the British Isles the possibilities are wide.
Essentially we must decide from what part of the globe the
air supply is likely to be coming, and the chief doubt which
can arise as to the future course of temperature comes mainly
from the same points which make any forecasting uncertain,
namely, the difficulty of gauging the general synoptic
situation and the consequent flow of air.

But certain things as a general rule we shall know. So
far as the British Isles are concerned, the great reservoirs
of cold air in winter will be Europe and Siberia to the
eastward, Greenland and the frozen Arctic Seas to
northward.

When light gradients for east and north-east winds cover
Great Britain, and a dry chilly air favours nocturnal
radiation, then "home-brewing" will be added to
"importing" of cold and the hardest frosts may be
developed. Then we often find the temperature 10° or 20°
lower in the most inland stations of England and Ireland,
and the isotherms gradually increase round these cold

centres. When we look at a synoptic chart for Europe for
7 a.m. we find, on these occasions, that Britain and Ireland
are separate islands of cold on the general thermal slope
from a cold continent to the warm North Atlantic.

From the fact that frost depends on radiation, we can readily
explain why cold can vary so much with locality. The least
breath of wind or any local influence may interfere with the
free play of radiation, and so we find two places only a few
miles apart one of which records 10° or 15° lower than the
other.

The reservoir of warm air in winter will be the Atlantic
and particularly the subtropical part.

The reservoirs of the hottest air in summer will be Europe
and North Africa, and the reservoirs of cool air in summer
will be the North Atlantic and the Arctic Ocean.

ADIABATIC EFFECTS

As to the second main cause of change of temperature,
namely, adiabatic change due to change of pressure, it is
not necessary to say much here in so far as local developments are concerned, because these received a measure of
attention in the chapter on the Upper Air and in connection
with the formation of cloud and rain.

An important effect, however, is liable to arise in the
course of the travel of the air, at least if it be polar air.
In tracing trajectories of polar air the author has noticed
numerous cases where at some early stage in its history
a mass of surface polar air would be moving with high
speed and would have a relatively low pressure and low
temperature. Later on, in the course of a journey southward,
and whilst it was spreading under tropical air, it would be
noted that the speed of the polar air diminished steadily,
its pressure rose steadily, and its temperature also rose
appreciably. An estimation of the various causes at work
showed that about half the rise of temperature might be of
adiabatic origin, i.e. due to compression, whilst the remainder

of the rise of temperature resulted from heat acquired from the surface of the sea or land.

Sometimes the opposite effect is noticed, i.e. a wedge of polar air retreats from under the tropical air, losing pressure and gaining speed, and also falling in temperature.

The temperature and pressure of tropical air are not so much affected by travel, because the tropical air, being lighter than the polar air, is always on top and is then not so liable to be compressed appreciably. It may, however, suffer some reduction of pressure near the centres of developing cyclones.

THE " BLIZZARD " AND THE " BARBER "

A very striking example of lowered temperature brought by wind is found in the " blizzards " of the United States. These are cold snaps which come with a high wind, as opposed to the calm frost of anticyclones. They are the result of the passage of the rear of cyclones or of V-shaped depressions in the winter months, with strong north-westerly winds, blowing off a frozen continent with a temperature many degrees below zero, and with consequences which are very destructive to life.

Another disagreeable form of cold is found in the St. Lawrence Gulf. Sometimes with a high wind the air becomes much colder than the open water. The latter being relatively hot begins to smoke, and the vapour freezes into peculiarly sharp spicules. The poudré snow crystals of the north-west are usually small, dry six-sided petals, and, though penetrating as sand, they are soft. The latter kind of snow is so sharp that, when driven by a gale it nearly cuts the skin off the face. Hence the popular name of the " barber ", which is applied to this phenomenon. The same name of " barber " is applied to another phase of cold along the coasts of Nova Scotia and New England. When a vessel is caught by a gale of wind in a cold arctic current, the spray freezes the moment it touches the deck or rigging. Every block is turned into a lump of ice ; men get coated with ice ; and sometimes such a weight of ice is formed on the bow that the stern is lifted out of the water and the ship becomes unmanageable for want of steering power.

MODIFYING INFLUENCE OF CLOUD AND WEATHER

The primary source of heat being the sun, we should, other things being equal, get the greatest heat where there is the least cloud ; that is to say generally in anticyclones. This, however, cannot be laid down as the general rule without modifications. In the belt of anticyclones which surround the world about the line of the tropics, some of the greatest known heats are recorded, notably in the Sahara and in Australia. But in higher latitudes the sun has a powerful enemy in outward radiation. In summer the sun is more powerful, and we get hot days with cold nights. In winter when the sun is low, radiation into space exceeds the radiation from a low sun, and clear weather is cold. When, therefore, we consider in general terms the influence of a clear sky on warmth, we must always take into consideration the time of year and latitude.

With regard to cloud, on the other hand, in England during the summer cloudy or rainy weather is cold because it cuts off the sun, independent of any chill of its own. In winter, on the contrary, rainy weather is warm, partly because an overcast sky prevents loss of heat by radiation. In the tropics cloudy weather is colder than a bright day, because the rays of the sun are obstructed ; but if there is little wind, a cloudy day is more oppressive to men than one with sunshine. Near the Equator there is very little night cooling by radiation, owing to the excessive amount of vapour in the air.

We may sum up these effects of sky briefly thus : In winter wind, cloud, and rain in temperate regions tend to raise the temperature, as they check outward radiation ;

calm on the contrary tends to produce frost. In summer wind, cloud, and rain are cooling influences as they mitigate the effects of solar radiation ; calm, on the contrary, leads to heat because it means less turbulence and allows the sun's heat to be communicated more continuously to the same surface air.

We may, in fact, look at the opposing forces of inward and outward radiation as in a state of constant conflict, whilst water vapour in some shape forms, as it were, a blanket for the earth, and saves her from being burnt up and frozen alternately. The incessant circulation of the atmosphere sometimes eddies in a cyclonic form, and develops dense cloud, which shields the earth from the radiation of the season and latitude ; at other times the circulation of the air eddies in an anticyclone, and the clear, dry, calm atmosphere gives full play to radiation, and some extreme of heat or cold is then developed. And all the time the air movement tends to improve the distribution of the heat and cold.

PRIMARY AND SECONDARY EFFECTS OF WARM AND COLD AREAS

We shall conclude with one important reflection. We know that heat is the prime mover of all atmospheric circulation ; why, then, do the great local differences of temperature have so little influence on the sequence of weather ? The greatest diurnal ranges are found in anti-cyclones, which are also associated with the steadiest weather ; and in wedges, where we find strong contrasts of heat and cold, these local differences of temperature are certainly not the cause of the cyclone and rain which follow soon. At the same time it is certain, for example, that the persistent anticyclone over Siberia during the winter months is caused by the radiation cold of that great continental area, and that it exercises a very considerable influence on the general circulation both whilst it exists and when it

commences to disperse ; also that the opposite seasonal
tendency in summer for high pressures to accumulate over
the oceans and lows over the continents arises from thermal
causes.

We must therefore allow that in the general circulation
of the air over the globe the direction of the currents will
be profoundly modified in this indirect manner by the
surface temperatures of the earth and sea. So that we have
the paradox that though the relatively fleeting day to day
changes of temperature in any country are the product of
the various synoptic situations, yet the areas favoured
by the more permanent high and low pressure systems are
themselves largely determined by the surface of the globe
and the part it plays in promoting radiation or mitigating
its effects and in conserving or distributing heat.

BIBLIOGRAPHY

The Life History of Surface Air Currents. W. N. Shaw and R. G. K.
Lempfert. London : Meteorological Office Mem., No. 1.
Bartholomew's Physical Atlas, vol. iii. Atlas of Meteorology, West-
minster, 1899.
Manual of Meteorology. Vol. ii : *Comparative Meteorology.* Sir Napier
Shaw. Camb. Univ. Press.

CHAPTER IX

DIURNAL VARIATION OF WEATHER

DIURNAL PHENOMENA

THE underlying principle here is that diurnal variation modifies rather than alters the general character of the weather, which is determined in the main by the surrounding distribution of pressure. In this matter diurnal are like local variations, but there is one important difference— that diurnal variations introduce us for the first time in this book to the consideration of the true nature of meteorological periodicities. From the variations which run through their entire course in one day we can readily pass to those whose period is one year, or even a longer cycle.

We shall commence with an account of the nature of the diurnal variation of temperature, as that is the most obvious of all meteorological phenomena. It is evident to all that, whatever the temperature of the day or season may be, the nights are in a general way colder than the days. We also know almost by instinct whether it is a generally cold or hot day, and equally instinctively we allow for the difference of day and night. Put into the formal language of ordinary meteorology, the general heat or cold of the day is expressed by the number which gives the mean temperature of the day; while the diurnal variation is given by the numbers which denote how much the thermometer was above or below the average at each hour.

DIURNAL VARIATION OF TEMPERATURE

If we examine thermograms we find many irregular changes of temperature; the one in Fig. 31, for example, is rather an extreme case ; but when the mean temperature for every hour is taken on a great many days, the irregularities balance out and the daily tendency is reflected in a fairly smooth mean curve. The mean curve signifies that in a general way, allowing for all sorts of irregularities, there is a solar diurnal influence, which has its greatest and least values at such and such hours. But we must most carefully avoid two conclusions : first, that the mean variation represents any abstract entity, which might be applied as a correction to the observed temperature at any hour so as to deduce the mean temperature of the day ; and, second, that because we do not see a diurnal variation

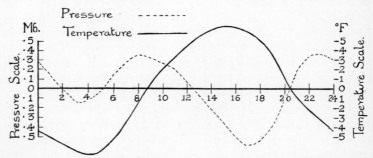

FIG. 37.—Mean Diurnal Variation of Temperature and Pressure at Kew Observatory in July.

on the trace for every day, therefore there is no such thing as solar diurnal influence. Temperature, like every other element of weather, is the balance of the general changes and diurnal variations.

In the British Isles temperature is usually at a maximum about two hours after local noon in winter and about three hours after noon in summer, and at a mimimum about sunrise. Fig. 37 shows the nature of the variation at Kew Observatory in July. Relative humidity varies in almost exactly the opposite way, i.e. it is at a minimum in the afternoon about the time of maximum temperature and it is at a maximum in the early morning about the time of minimum temperature. The explanation of this is quite simple ; the actual moisture content of the air does not vary greatly throughout the day, and hence with roughly the same moisture content the approach to saturation is much closer when the temperature is low at night and much less close when the temperature rises during the day.

The range of the mean diurnal variation of temperature depends on " continentality ", on latitude, and on altitude.

In the previous chapter we have explained that owing to the great capacity of the oceans as compared with land surfaces for storing and distributing heat, there tends over the oceans to be a considerable suppression of the ordinary day and night changes of temperature. Actually the diurnal range of temperature of the surface water of the oceans is only about 1° F near the Equator and only about a quarter of a degree in the Atlantic north of the British Isles. By contrast the temperature of the surface of the soil in Europe may vary throughout the 24 hours by 50° and in the Sahara desert it may vary by 120°, even though at a depth of 3 feet in the ground the day to night change of temperature becomes almost imperceptible.

With increasing distance from the oceans and larger seas we find an increase in all meteorological elements in what is called the " continentality factor ". The more continental a climate is, the greater is the diurnal variation, as well as the annual range, of temperature, and the more nearly does the time of maximum temperature during the day or in the course of the seasons approach to coincidence with the time of the maximum altitude of the sun.

It is only for places where hourly records of temperature are kept that we can arrive at the exact diurnal variation and its range. What is known as the mean daily range of temperature is not exactly the same thing, being the mean difference between the highest and lowest temperatures reached on individual days and thus being as a rule rather larger than the range of the mean diurnal variation ; but we know the values of the mean daily range for a great many places because at these places records are kept of the extreme temperatures for each day ; and we may take these values, other things being equal, as indicating roughly how the diurnal variations at different places would compare with one another. At the Scilly Isles, for example, the average daily range of temperature in January is 6·8° F and in July 8·6° F, whilst at London these ranges become 8·5° and 16·7° respectively, and at Warsaw, far from the sea, they become 9·0° and 18·7° respectively, though these three places do not differ greatly in latitude.

With increasing latitude the daily range of temperature in temperate regions becomes smaller, other things being equal ; but in high latitudes the non-periodic changes become relatively more important.

The effect of altitude is generally to diminish the diurnal variation very considerably at stations of the peak type or in the free air. At the top of Ben Nevis, for example, the ranges of the mean diurnal variation in January and July are 0·5° F and 4·0° F respectively, whilst at Fort William the corresponding ranges are 1·8° F and 8·5 ° F respectively. At the Eiffel Tower in Paris, about 1,000 feet above ground level, the January and July ranges are 2·0° F and 9·5° F, whereas near ground level in Paris they are 5·9° F and 16·4° F respectively.

DIURNAL VARIATION OF PRESSURE

Atmospheric pressure all over the world has a characteristic diurnal variation. Its most constant feature is a twelve-hourly oscillation with its maxima at about 10 a.m. and 10 p.m. local mean time. The amplitude of the oscillation is greatest and the oscillation is usually very obvious in tropical latitudes. In tropical seas the daily range of pressure is about 2½ mb. and on land areas it may rise to about 4 mb. It diminishes towards the poles and, indeed, in temperate latitudes it is only conspicuous in the combined average values for a month or some longer period, because the non-periodic changes in pressure associated with the passage of cyclones and anticyclones are so relatively large that they mask the small twelve-hourly oscillation.

At London, for example, the mean amplitude of the semi-diurnal variation throughout the year is 0·35 mb., at Aberdeen 0·25 mb., and at Lerwick 0·13 mb. Fig. 37 shows that at Kew Observatory the semi-diurnal variation is superposed on a 24-hour variation.

The 24-hourly variation of pressure at stations near sea level is frequently less obvious and is less regular and more dependent on locality. On mountains, however, there is an important and regular whole day variation of pressure, which arises in the following way. The day-time rise of temperature in the lower layers of atmosphere expands these layers so that when temperature is at a maximum more of the atmosphere lies above a given mountain station than when temperature is at its minimum. Thus the observations at the Ben Nevis and Fort William observatories, which differ in altitude by 4,235 feet, suggest an average total expansion and contraction of some 22 feet on the part of the layer of atmosphere lying between these two levels. At mountain stations, from this effect, the barometric pressure is usually at its maximum about 4 p.m. and at its minimum about 6 a.m.

DIURNAL VARIATION OF WIND

The diurnal variations in the various meteorological elements all arise primarily from the daily effects of the sun in raising the temperature of the air—especially the air near the ground—and from the turbulence induced in consequence, and from the corresponding loss of heat by outward radiation from the earth, air, clouds, etc., at night.

In wind, as we have indicated in an earlier chapter, there is from this cause a very pronounced diurnal variation, the commonest feature of which is that in most places the speed of the surface air increases gradually from sunrise to about 2 p.m. ; after a few hours it falls fairly rapidly until just after sunset, and then slightly, reaching its lowest point usually just about sunrise. This variation is characteristic of settled weather ; it is also predominantly a land variation and almost vanishes over the open sea. In fact, the magnitude of the variation depends pretty much on the daily range of temperature of the floor over which the air flows. During disturbed weather the general changes may obliterate the characteristic variation entirely.

Before giving the explanation of this diurnal variation of the surface wind, we must refer to another fact, which has been established by records maintained at the top of the Eiffel Tower in Paris and by upper air observations generally, namely, that at heights of the order of 1,000 feet and higher there is a reversed effect. The speed at these levels is definitely reduced during the day, and it is at night that the highest speed is attained. These variations at ground level and at higher levels and the connection between them are explained by ground friction and convectional turbulence. In the chapter on Wind and Calm we have mentioned that friction with the ground and collision with obstacles exercise so powerful a retarding effect on the moving surface air that, if it were not for the more or less frequent accessions of momentum received from above, the surface air would soon be brought to rest. At night there is little turbulence, i.e. little exchange of air between ground level and the higher levels, and therefore the surface level receives correspondingly little momentum from the freely moving air above. Thus the wind at the surface dies down. During the day, and especially on a bright day with active convection, masses of quickly moving air from the higher levels are continually exchanging position with masses of slow-moving air from the lower levels. The result is to bring the speeds at surface and at upper levels more nearly into agreement, i.e. to speed up the surface air and to slow down the upper air. The effect, of course, extends only so far up as active daytime convection ; under average conditions it is certainly prominent at heights of 1,000 to 2,000 feet.

Fig. 38 shows very nicely the manner in which the speeds of the surface wind and the wind at 1,000 feet above the surface are affected throughout the day by the varying degree of turbulence in operation. In the first place we note that the wind at the top of the Eiffel Tower is always much greater than it is near ground level ; this demonstrates

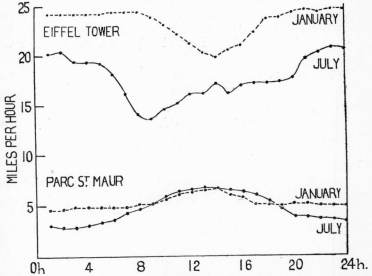

FIG. 38.—Mean Diurnal Variation of Wind on Eiffel Tower and Parc St. Maur in January and July.

the effect of ground friction in reducing the speed at ground level. Next, looking at the July curves, we note that during the forenoon while the surface wind is rising in speed the wind at 1,000 feet is being pulled down considerably in speed. This is a result of the mixing of air at these two levels under the influence of the daytime convectional turbulence caused by heating of the ground by the sun. In the evening the two curves separate again as convectional turbulence dies down. In January a similar result is seen, but on the whole the two curves are more widely separated than in July, because on the whole convectional effects are correspondingly diminished ; also for the same reasons the period in the day when the curves approach is briefer and nearer to midday.

These results are averages deduced from many observations, but the freshening of the wind during the day and the fall to calm or almost calm at night are characteristic phenomena of fine settled weather. In unsettled conditions the more general weather changes may mask or obliterate the diurnal variation and on cloudy days it is but little apparent.

From an analysis of the results of pilot balloon ascents J. Durward has reached the following conclusions regarding the winds at higher levels.

" (a) Winds up to heights of 3,000 feet have a minimum velocity which occurs about noon.

" (b) The tendency is for this minimum to occur later the higher one goes.

" (c) At 4,000 feet and 6,000 feet the number of observations is insufficient to indicate exactly what happens ; but the behaviour of easterly and westerly winds appears to be different. West winds decrease by day and east winds increase."

(He considers, however, that this difference may be a local effect or may even be fortuitous.)

" (d) In general a decrease of velocity is accompanied by a backing which may amount to as much as 20°."

All that has been said above applies to conditions on land. Buchan in analysing the observations of the expedition of H.M.S. *Challenger* found that at sea there was an indication of a semi-diurnal variation of wind, but the variation was not regular and was not the same in different oceans. There is quite a marked semi-diurnal variation in the anemograph records of the Bell Rock Lighthouse, which is situated 12 miles from the nearest part of the coast

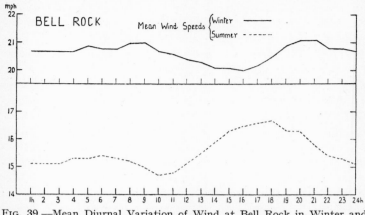

FIG. 39.—Mean Diurnal Variation of Wind at Bell Rock in Winter and Summer.

of Scotland. Fig. 39 shows the mean diurnal variation of wind speed in summer and winter at Bell Rock.

DIURNAL PROCESSES

So far in this chapter we have dealt with average conditions, but we wish now to see what happens in the varied conditions of weather and of atmospheric structure which may be experienced on different days. We now turn therefore to a more detailed examination of the diurnal processes going on in the atmosphere and first we take the daytime processes.

The incoming solar radiation in clear weather, as we have seen in the chapter on the Upper Air, is not absorbed to a very great extent directly by the atmosphere, but mainly by the earth's surface ; the heated surface emits radiation of longer wave-length and a great part of this (50 per cent at least) is then absorbed by a relatively shallow layer of atmosphere of the order of 100 feet in depth ; also a certain amount of heat is communicated to the surface air by direct contact with the ground or sea surface. Our first concern in understanding the diurnal events of any particular day is the extent to which the daily heat thus received in the surface layer is retained, and the extent to which it is distributed to other layers of the atmosphere. If the lapse rate of temperature near the ground is equal or nearly equal to the dry adiabatic lapse rate it will be seen that convection will set in quickly and the warmed masses of air will be continually transferred to higher levels, and in brief, though there will be a slight lag in the transference of the heat upwards it will tend continually to be nearly uniformly distributed throughout the total depth of atmosphere in which this convection is taking place. In these circumstances it is obvious that the daytime rise of temperature in the air near the ground cannot be nearly so rapid as it would be if some check could be placed upon the convectional activity. Now it will be readily understood that in polar air the lapse rate of temperature near the ground will nearly always be fairly high, because such air, starting from cold regions and passing over ever warmer land and sea on its way southward, is continually being warmed from the bottom, and thus is kept well stirred up.

Equatorial air, on the other hand, is generally moving under conditions which make for greater stability, for it is generally losing heat from its surface layers by contact with successively colder sea or land as it passes from subtropical to temperate regions. As indicating the difference between polar air and equatorial air in the first thousand feet above ground level, it may be mentioned that the average fall of temperature in the first thousand feet, as deduced from observations made on aeroplane ascents mostly during the morning hours (see Table III in Chapter III) is, in the case of polar air 3·1° F in winter and 4·5° F in summer, whilst in the case of equatorial air it is 2·0° F and 2·9° F respectively.

Fig 40 shows the average diurnal variations of temperature in May at Eskdalemuir Observatory on days of polar air and equatorial air respectively. The sun rises about 5 a.m. and from that hour until about 9 a.m. it will be seen that temperature rises steadily, and at much the same rates in polar and equatorial air ; this is because during this period there is as yet little mixing of different layers of air.   About 9 a.m., however, the approximate parallelism between the two curves ceases.   The curve for equatorial days continues on a regular course, but that for polar days assumes very noticeably a different direction, owing apparently to the setting in of active convection which distributes some of the absorbed solar heat to higher levels.   This is proved by the formation of clouds of cumulus type which in turn, by intercepting part of the sun's radiation

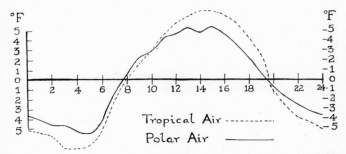

Fig. 40.—Diurnal Variation of Temperature at Eskdalemuir Observatory in May on days of tropical and days of polar air.

at a higher level, further lessen the rate of rise of temperature in the surface layer.   Thus in the course of the day the polar curve rises to a less extent than does the equatorial curve.

After 17 h. and until 21 h. temperature in the two cases falls again rapidly, but this time rather less rapidly in the polar air, probably because the greater turbulence existing in this air takes more time to die down.

The whole result, as will be seen, is to reduce the diurnal range of temperature in polar air in this month to roughly three-quarters of that in equatorial air.   The consequences of the different atmospheric structure in polar and equatorial air are seen also in the cloud and sunshine experienced. During the summer months daytime convection is usually so active in polar air as to result in the formation of a good deal of cumulus cloud by midday and these clouds in turn cut off a good deal of the afternoon sunshine. This is particularly so with maritime polar air. Those bright, clear summer mornings that are described popularly as being " too bright to last " are the typical polar air mornings. In winter and spring, however, the total insolation is not as a rule sufficient to upset appreciably the stability of the polar air, so that in these seasons days of polar air remain bright and are often characterized by almost continuous sunshine.

Equatorial air has almost the opposite characteristics. Normally it has considerable stability in the surface layers, though its fairly high content of water vapour results frequently in the mornings opening with a certain amount of low cloud. A good deal of the incoming solar radiation is absorbed at this cloud and goes to evaporating the cloud before much radiation can reach the ground. Then, however, the greater stability of the air in the vertical direction allows a lot of heat to be taken up by the lower layers before much convection sets in. The tendency thus in equatorial air is for the afternoons in summer at least to be both warm and sunny. If, on the other hand, the day starts clear then it probably will remain bright and be a day of considerable heat for the season of the year.

Thus, as a general rule, there is in summer considerably more sunshine in equatorial than in polar air, more especially in the southern part of the British Isles ; there, in fact, every hour from 9 a.m. to 6 p.m. has an " expectation " with equatorial air of at least 60 per cent of possible sunshine.

In winter, however, these conditions are reversed. Equatorial air, becoming chilled to its dew-point in its passage over the cold land, tends to be misty or cloudy to an extent which winter sunshine cannot clear ; and in the north of the country especially there is usually no sunshine, but much cloud or actual precipitation. The maximum of sunshine in winter is experienced on polar days of light or moderate wind.

These differences between polar and equatorial air are important from the point of view of forecasting the weather of the day, and the consideration of the origin of the air affords a ready indication of the relative degree of stability or instability of the lower layers of atmosphere and the type of diurnal variation to be expected.

DIURNAL VARIATION OF RAINFALL

It would be almost useless to attempt to discuss the diurnal variation of rainfall without reference to the manner in which the rain is produced and to the atmospheric structure existing at the time. The rain with which we have been mainly concerned so far is that connected with cyclones and falling chiefly at the warm and cold fronts.

It might be thought that the bad weather at fronts would be quite unaffected by diurnal events but this does not seem to be the case. Possibly it is because of the varying effect on the vertical atmospheric structure, but, anyway, there are distinct diurnal effects both in the case of warm fronts and in the case of cold fronts. In the case of warm fronts there is some tendency for the rain to reach its maximum in the latter part of the night or the early morning ; and, particularly in summer and over land, the rain may cease in the middle of the day and early afternoon, or at all events fall off considerably. In the case of cold fronts, on the other hand, there is a very marked tendency indeed for most rain to occur in the afternoon, and there is a slight tendency to a secondary maximum about 4 a.m.

The average diurnal variations of cold front and warm front rainfall respectively are set out in Fig. 41. The figures give the total rain falling in each hour for five stations in different parts of the British Isles, over a period of three years. It will be seen that the two kinds of rainfall behave almost in opposite fashion in the matter of diurnal variation. It will also be noticed incidentally that the total amount of cold front rainfall for the whole day is roughly only half of the warm front rainfall ; and that even at the time of day of maximum incidence of the cold front rain the average amount of rainfall to be expected in an hour if a cold front is passing is only about the same as is to be expected if a warm front is passing, though the time in question is the time when the warm front rain is at its minimum.

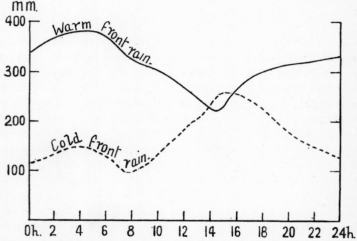

Fig. 41.—Diurnal Variations of Rainfall at Warm and Cold Fronts.

The reason is chiefly that the cold front rain comes usually in short showers, whilst the warm front rain is more or less continuous.

Effects similar to those just described may be seen in typical climatic conditions. For example, at European coastal stations the rainfall is mostly of the type produced by upsliding currents, i.e. it is either warm front rainfall or orographic rainfall. The characteristic diurnal variation of rainfall in such cases has a maximum between about 4 a.m. and 8 a.m. (local time), a generally low level from 10 a.m.

to 6 p.m., and a slight secondary maximum from about 10 p.m. to midnight.

At inland continental stations and at tropical stations generally, on the other hand, the rainfall is largely of the type known as instability rainfall, which will be dealt with more fully below. Its diurnal variation follows closely that described above for cold front or squall line rainfall ; it has a very pronounced maximum usually about 2 to 5 p.m., a slight secondary maximum about 2 to 4 a.m., and the chief minimum about 8 to 10 a.m. Fig. 42 illustrates these effects.

In the chapter on the Upper Air and also in the present chapter we have referred to the conditions determining stability or instability of the atmosphere in the matter of vertical movements, whilst in the chapter on the structure of a cyclone we have shown how rain is usually produced by continued upward movement of air at warm fronts or as the result of topographical conditions. It will readily be seen that even without the presence of cyclones or mountains, sufficient upward air movement to cause local showers might conceivably result, with the assistance of diurnal processes, from local surface warming of the air, provided the air initially is sufficiently well charged with moisture, and provided the initial lapse rate of temperature borders on instability. Very favourable conditions for such occurrences exist over the tropical oceans and even more markedly along tropical coasts where a horizontal gradient of temperature from land to sea assists the development of instability on a big scale. In the East Indies, for example, the diurnal heating with great regularity results during the forenoon in the formation of great cumulus and cumulo-nimbus clouds, the tops of which later on may reach to heights of 5 or 6 kilometres ; in the afternoon heavy showers and thunderstorms are the customary sequence. Rain occurring in this way is sometimes classed as non-isobaric rain in the sense that the isobars in themselves give little or no guide to this rain, which is rather to be regarded as

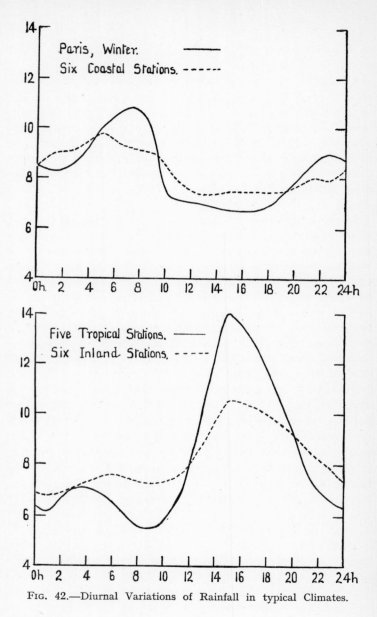

Fig. 42.—Diurnal Variations of Rainfall in typical Climates.

a diurnal development in a suitably moist and unstable atmosphere. Now, since such rain is the product of the condensation from an ascensional current of air, then the more violent the uptake the greater must be the down-draught in some adjacent region. It is, indeed, more in accord with dynamical principles to think of the (sinking) adjacent colder air as pushing up the (rising) heated air, even in cases where the movement has obviously been initiated through the surface heating of the air over a given area. Atmospheric circulation brought about in this way works as a " heat engine " and, as in other " heat engines ", continuous movement can take place so long as the source of heat is lower than the source of cold.

In particular we can alternatively set up vertical movement by cooling the upper air instead of by warming the lower air. To take an example again from the East Indies, in addition to a principal maximum of daily rainfall in the late afternoon there is a secondary maximum of rainfall in the later part of the night, which is probably associated with instability caused by cooling of the upper clouds by nocturnal radiation. The effect is noticeable in Fig. 42 in the curve relating to tropical stations.

To take a further example, practically the whole of the heavy rain of the Doldrums is non-isobaric or instability rainfall.

BIBLIOGRAPHY

The Structure of the Atmosphere as affected by Diurnal Variations.
    A. H. R. Goldie. Edin. Proc. Roy. Soc., vol. xlvii, pt. iv, No. 25
    (1927).
*Characteristics of Rainfall Distribution in Homogeneous Air Currents
    and at Surfaces of Discontinuity.* A. H. R. Goldie. London :
    Meteorological Office Geoph. Mem., No. 53 (1931).

M

CHAPTER X

LOCAL VARIATION OF WEATHER

CHARACTERISTIC EFFECTS

THIS chapter groups conveniently a class of dependent phenomena which owe their origin to the influence of local obstacles or peculiarities on the development of weather. Within the same country some places are, for instance, on the average much colder or wetter than others. The local meteorologist who would forecast successfully must work out the peculiarities of his own district. Local is like diurnal weather in so far that the observed weather is the sum of the local variations and general causes. When the general are strong, the local are more or less masked ; when the general are weak the local become of primary importance.

If we watch the actual occurrence of any local peculiarity of weather we shall find that it is as a rule the intensity, and not the general character, which is altered. On a still frosty morning, for instance, two places a few miles apart may differ by 5° or 10° of temperature. The stillness and the radiation that produced the frosty morning are general and not local effects, but it is local peculiarities of exposure which have eliminated modifying effects and enabled radiation to act so much more effectively on the surface air in the one place than in the other. Again, an inch of rain may fall on a mountain side and a quarter of an inch on the same day in a valley not many miles away.

If, however, we consider the rainfall of longer periods, a month or a year, we shall find that the mountain station almost always receives more rain than the valley station and that the proportion remains fairly constant. This topographical effect is caused by the interference of the rising land with moisture-laden winds. We have already explained how the rainfall at the warm front of a depression is caused by the uprising of the warm current over the wedge of cold air in front of it. A mountain mass may act in the same way as a wedge of cold air and cause the uprising effect. Thus, for example, the west Highlands of Scotland receive heavy rain on days when strong equatorial air currents blow from south-westwards ; such rainfall is very common in winter when south-westerly winds are frequent and strong. Rain produced in this way is known as orographic rain. Even on the east coast of the British Isles orographic effects may be noted at times in east winds, but the land for the most part is too low for such effects to be conspicuous. Examples of orographic influence are to be found all over the world. For instance, in Ceylon the rainy seasons on the two sides of the island are in different months, which depend on the time when each coast is exposed to the prevailing monsoon. The south-west monsoon brings rain to the exposed west side of the island, and the dry season to the east coast. The north-east monsoon, on the contrary, first strikes the east coast and develops abundant rainfall there, while the west coast then enjoys its dry season. A similar sequence is observed on the opposite coasts of the island of Luzon, in the Philippines, and for a similar reason.

LOCAL VARIATION OF RAINFALL AT FRONTS

Even on cyclonic rainfall at fronts, however, there is an orographic influence. The effect of mountains is to delay the retreat of the wedge of cold air in front of the depressions, so that a very effective and lasting upsliding surface is formed over a mountainous region, with the consequence that the warm front rain is both amplified and prolonged. This effect is very conspicuous in the mountainous parts of the North of England, in Scotland, and in West Norway.

It may be of advantage to give some statistical information about warm and cold fronts, and the average amounts of rain connected with them in different districts, though in doing so we repeat the warning as to the limitations attaching to the value of averages when forecasting.

In the southern part of the British Isles roughly 30 per cent of the days of the year are characterized by the passage of either warm or cold fronts or both. In the northern parts of the country the frequency of occurrence of these phenomena is rather greater. This difference in frequency, however, is not so important as the difference in the average amounts of rainfall connected with fronts in different parts of the country. In the eastern coastal districts a day on which a warm front passes averages some 4 mm. of rain and a day with a cold front averages about 3 mm. or less. Amongst the higher land of the west and central parts, however, as represented for instance by Eskdalemuir Observatory in Dumfriesshire, it is found that the former type of day averages 10 mm. and the latter type about 6 mm. And in the very mountainous districts the amounts would run up to very much higher figures.

A more detailed way of conveying information is by means of the frequency of occurrence of specified amounts of rain, and this we give below, for three places, for days marked by the passage of fronts.

TABLE V

PERCENTAGE FREQUENCY OF AMOUNTS OF RAINFALL ON DAYS MARKED BY THE PASSAGE OF FRONTS

Amount of Rain	London (Kew Observatory)	Aberdeen	Dumfriesshire (Eskdalemuir Observatory)
mm.	%	%	%
0–1	38	41	12
1–5	33	29	32
5–10	18	15	28
10–15	5	9	12
15–20	3	3	8
20–25	2	2	2
More than 25	1	1	6

The table, for example, indicates that in London 38 per cent of the days of the type dealt with have less than 1 mm.

of rain, whilst only 1 per cent have more than 25 mm.
(1 inch) of rain. At Eskdalemuir, by contrast, only 12 per
cent of such days have less than 1 mm. of rain—and these
few we may remark occur chiefly in summer—whilst
6 per cent have over 25 mm. of rain.

Rain in Homogeneous Currents

Even on days when the air belongs to a current that is
more or less homogeneous in the horizontal direction (i.e.
days on which no actual front passes), small amounts of
rain may occur from topographical or from instability effects.
We give below another table indicating, for such days, the
percentage frequency on which more than 1 mm. of rain falls.

TABLE VI

FREQUENCY OF OCCURRENCE OF MORE THAN 1 MM. OF RAIN ON DAYS OF
TROPICAL AND POLAR AIR

		Summer %	Winter %
Polar Air	London	25	21
	Aberdeen	33	32
	Eskdalemuir	21	31
Tropical Air	London	23	35
	Aberdeen	26	28
	Eskdalemuir	25	69

The notable thing about this table is that, with one
exception, it indicates a frequency of roughly 1 in 3, or
1 in 4 for amounts of more than 1 mm. of rain. The
exception is the case of Eskdalemuir in winter, where the
frequency rises to 2 in three days. The effect here is thus
a complication of topography and season. In point of fact
a current of tropical air at Eskdalemuir gives on an average
in winter about 6 mm. of rain and in summer rather over
2 mm. of rain per day from purely topographical causes.

The sum total of orographic effects is so important as
to cause the average annual rainfall over even the small
area of the British Isles to vary from 20 inches along the
Thames estuary to over 150 inches in the English Lake

District, parts of the Welsh mountains, and parts of the Western Highlands of Scotland.

CLOUD, SUNSHINE, AND TEMPERATURE

The distribution of cloudiness over the country varies in very much the same way as rainfall. The amount of sunshine, on the other hand, depending as it does (for places in the same latitude) on the extent to which the sky is free from cloud, varies in the opposite way to rainfall. Thus the sunniest parts of the British Isles are round the coasts and in valleys, and the estuaries of large rivers, whilst the most sunless parts, taking the year as a whole, are on the tops of the western mountains. Places on the south-east coast of England, for example, receive on the average 1,800 hours per annum, the flat Island of Tiree has about 1,480 hours, the top of Ben Nevis only 750 hours, whilst Fort William at the foot of the mountain has about 1,100 hours.

From what has been said already in this book it will be appreciated that in so far as local variation in the same latitude is concerned the temperature is controlled mainly by altitude and by distance from the sea. At times when the atmosphere is well stirred up, as, for instance, by convection on a summer day or by strong winds, the effect of altitude is to reduce the temperature by about 1° F per 300 feet of rise. Calm radiation weather, however, at night or in winter, tends to invert these conditions and may even result in places in valleys being colder than places on mountain sides or tops. Extremely low winter night temperatures characterize high valleys.

The presence of the sea or large bodies of water has a modifying influence. Places far inland, as we have shown in the previous chapter, tend to have higher daily maximum temperatures and lower daily minimum temperatures, or, in other words, are characterized by a large daily range of temperature. Thus Cambridge during a " heat wave " may have an afternoon temperature of 90° F or more,

whilst Yarmouth at the same time may be 10° cooler.
The inland places are similarly characterized by a more
considerable annual range of temperature.   The differences
between the mean temperatures of the warmest and coldest
months at Scilly, London, and Warsaw respectively are
15·5°, 23·8°, and 39·3°.

The total effect of local influences is best seen in maps
or tables of " normal values ", by which is meant averages
over a long period, usually thirty-five years. For information
of much interest in connection with British weather and of
much practical value the reader is referred to the *Book of
Normals* mentioned below.

BIBLIOGRAPHY

Book of Normals of Meteorological Elements for the British Isles.
Section III (containing maps of the normal distribution of
sunshine, rainfall, and temperature).   London : H.M. Stationery
Office.   Price 1s. 6d.
Climate. C. E. P. Brooks. London : Ernest Benn, Ltd. 10s. 6d.

CHAPTER XI

LINE SQUALLS, THUNDERSTORMS

LINE SQUALLS

IN certain cases the phenomena occurring at the cold front
or squall line of a depression attain more than usual violence.
We have already explained that the cold front, or—in the
case of an occluded depression—the trough line, is in general
associated with a line of squalls and we must picture to
ourselves a long, narrow band of rain and wind sweeping
across the country, broadside on, like a wall or curtain,
at much the same speed as the depression itself. This
speed, however, bears no relation to that of the wind in the
squall.

The instability at a cold front may become very marked
if the cold and the warm air currents on the two sides of the
front differ considerably in temperature and if their
directions are considerably inclined to one another. In that
case the front sweeps rapidly across the country more like
a tidal wave of cold air, generally accompanied by a violent
squall of wind, and a sharp fall of rain, hail, or snow, always
by an abrupt rise of pressure and fall of temperature and
sometimes by thunder. To these cases the name line squall
is given. These phenomena had been studied in considerable
detail many years before the Bergen theory of the depression
was advanced and indicated more clearly the nature of their
association with depressions.

One of the earliest examples to be studied was the famous
Eurydice squall of 24th March, 1878, which capsized the
British man-of-war of that name and caused one of the
greatest disasters that had befallen the British Navy for

many years.   Two of the diagrams prepared when this squall was first studied are reproduced below.

In Fig. 60, under weather-types, we give a chart of a large portion of the northern hemisphere for 24th March, 1878, at 0.43 p.m. G.M.T.   On that date a large and irregular depression was centred somewhere over southern Scandinavia, so that the general run of the isobars over the British Isles was from about N.N.W. to S.S.E.   The squall which we have now to consider belonged to one of the

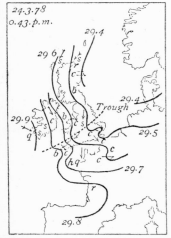

FIG. 43.—The Eurydice Squall, Iso-   FIG. 44.—The Eurydice Squall. Area
bars and Wind at 0.43 p.m.   covered by squall at 3 p.m.

numerous secondaries which hardly show on the chart and it was associated with the bend in the isobars indicated by the dotted line marked " trough " in Fig. 43. This bend appears to have been of the nature of a V-shaped depression, in some way secondary to the irregular depression covering the southern part of Scandinavia. In the course of the day the trough of the V wheeled round a point near the Scaw, in Denmark, like the spoke of a wheel.   Fig. 43 shows the position of the trough at 0.43 p.m. ; the front line of the

crescent-shaped shaded area in Fig. 44 shows approximately
the position of the trough at 3 p.m.; and by 6 p.m. the
trough passed in a curved line from Yarmouth, through
the Straits of Dover, into Normandy. By reason of this
wheeling motion, different portions of the trough moved
with very different velocities. Between the hours just
named, the northern portion of the trough moved across
England at the rate of only 13 miles an hour, while the
extreme south-westerly edge traversed the country at the
rate of no less than 48 miles an hour. The portion which
struck the *Eurydice* was going at the rate of 38 miles an hour.

So far we have considered the motion of the V as a whole.
In Fig. 43 the wind was from about west in front, and from
north-west in rear of the V, but no well-defined area of rain
was then developed. By 3 p.m., however, the phenomenon
was so much better defined that Mr. Clement Ley was able
to construct the diagram given in Fig. 44 as applying to
that hour. In that figure the shaded portion shows the area
over which rain or snow was falling at the moment; the
solid arrows give the general sweep of the surface-winds,
the dotted ones those of the upper currents. Abercromby
showed further that the front of the rain-area was essentially
coincident with the trough of the V, which we see about
two hours earlier in Fig. 43, so that we evidently have to
deal with a V of that class in which the rain is in the rear
of the trough. At every station, after the wind had been
from the west, with a cloudy sky in the morning, the clouds
gradually banked up ominously to the north-west; then
rain or snow came on with a tremendous squall, while the
wind jumped round to north-west. After the first burst
had moderated, rain or snow continued for a longer or shorter
interval till the sky cleared again.

H.M.S. *Eurydice* was a full-rigged corvette, homeward
bound from the West Indies. At 3.45 p.m.—three-quarters
of an hour later than that for which the chart given in Fig. 44
was constructed—she was off Ventnor, in the Isle of Wight,
running free before a nearly westerly wind, with all sail

set. At that moment she was struck by a squall from the north-west ; before sail could be shortened she went on to her beam-ends, and as the lee ports were open, she filled and foundered.

On the whole we have, therefore, to visualize a band-shaped area of rain, bounded in front by a line of squalls—in this case more than 400 miles long—sweeping broadside on across Great Britain at a rate varying from 13 to nearly 50 miles an hour. From this we can readily see how places many miles apart can be struck simultaneously at the same hour, and how applicable is the name of line squalls, which we have applied to this class of disturbance.

Though this high degree of development is not very common in Great Britain, it appears to be very frequent in other parts of the world. For instance, in Iowa, a similar kind of squall is peculiarly characteristic of summer weather. There it generally occurs after a spell of continued hot, rather sultry weather, the wind having blown steadily but moderately from the south or south-west, the barometer not changing much. In the north-west the storm-front will make its appearance ; threatening, dark, towering clouds, or at times an immense roll-like cloud, will approach ; the air cools rapidly as the storm-front comes nearer ; and, with a high, straight blow, bending young trees to the ground and driving the rain nearly level, the fierce storm passes over, while the barometer rises rapidly. Such a blow does not last long, but may be repeated with gradually weakened force at intervals. A steady pouring rain generally follows, after which the sky clears and the storm wind wheels back to the south-east, the weather being as hot as before the storm.

Many British and European thunderstorms are of the line-squall type. Following similarly on hot sultry weather, the storm-front will make its appearance in the west or north-west with the threatening clouds, and at times the immense roll-like cloud, and beyond this a peculiar light grey uniform sky. The dark low band of cloud passes over-head and heavy rain commences as the light grey cloud comes on. The first burst of rain is usually the heaviest, and after a longer or shorter period the rain usually clears off gradually. With this rain the sudden rise of the barometer is observed. The wind, which has fallen very light from the south-east or south as the clouds begin to bank up, comes in a violent squall from the west, about the time when the dark wreath passes overhead, and falls again shortly after the commencement of the heavy rain. The displacement of one current by another takes place in a manner similar to that already described in connection with cold fronts.

Fig. 45 shows the sequence of events as observed by Mr. G. A. Clarke in the case of a line squall which occurred at Aberdeen on 14th October, 1912. The four sketches of the squall cloud were made at intervals of two minutes, viz. at 10.24, 10.26, 10.28, and 10.30 G.M.T. The anemogram and barogram in the centre of the figure cover a period of seven hours centering at the time of the squall, which on this occasion characterized the transition from a S.S.W. to a W.N.W. wind. On one side of these records is the synoptic chart for 7 a.m. and on the other side the chart for 1 p.m.

On a synoptic chart a frequent indication of liability to a development of this sort is what is called in Germany a " gewitternase ", a nose-like prominence on the isobars of a shallow depression. With the depression centred to westward of the British Isles and the thunderstorm nose extending over France or Germany, we see that the eastward side of the nose will be characterized by light south-easterly winds. Diurnal heating over the hot central parts of the continent greatly raises the temperature of the lower layers of this light south-easterly current and increases the tendency to instability in the vertical direction. And especially in early summer this gives rise to an extremely unstable condition of affairs, because it increases the contrast between the south-easterly current over the continent and the cool westerly winds on the south side of the main depression. In many cases the result in the afternoon is an irruption or perhaps successive irruptions of cool westerly winds in successive

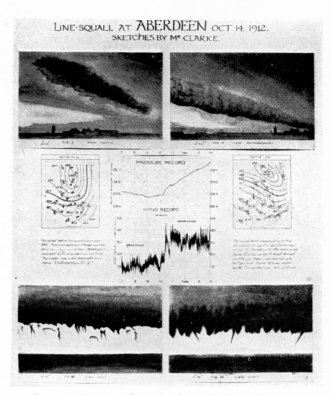

FIG. 45.   Line squall at Aberdeen, October 14th, 1912.

[*face p.* 172

thundersqualls. It may be noted in passing that this type of thunderstorm is the familiar one of sultry weather with the " thunder coming against the wind ", the wind before the thunder being generally south-easterly and after the thunder south-westerly, westerly, or north-westerly, the change sweeping on from westward.

In like manner the daily thunderstorm which occurs in so many countries at the time when the sea-breeze comes in, charging, as it were, the prevailing wind over the land, is due to a long vertical whirl with horizontal axis where the two currents meet, and the whole length can sometimes be watched gradually advancing inland from the coast. The so-called north-westers at Calcutta, during the hot season, belong to this last type.

PAMPEROS, SOUTHERLY BURSTERS

The word " pampero " is used in a very vague manner in the Argentine Republic and neighbouring States. Every south-west wind which blows from off the pampas is sometimes called a pampero ; and there is a still further confusion caused by calling dry dust-storms pamperos sucios, or dry pamperos. The true pampero may be described as a south-west wind, ushered in by a sudden short squall, usually accompanied by rain and thunder, with a very peculiar form of cloud-wreath. We shall describe these as given by D. Christison in the *Proceedings of the Scottish Meteorological Society*, No. lx, p. 330, and then we shall have no difficulty in recognizing a line squall as the source of the pampero.

The barometer always falls pretty steadily for from two to four days before the pampero, and always rises for some days after the squall.

Temperature is always very high before the squall, and then the sudden change of wind sends the thermometer rapidly down, sometimes as much as 33° in six hours.

Thunder accompanies about three out of four pamperos ;

but more or less rain always falls except in the rarest cases.

The wind before this class of pampero almost invariably blows moderately or gently for some days from easterly points, and then with a sudden burst the south-west wind comes down with its full strength, and, after blowing thus from ten to thirty minutes, either ceases entirely or continues with diminished force for a certain number of hours. In all cases but one the upper wind-currents have been seen to come from the north-west both before, during, and after the pampero.

The general appearance of a pampero will be best understood by a description of an actual squall. " In the early morning of a day in November, the wind blew rather strongly from the north-east. The sky was cloudy, but not overcast, save in the south-west horizon. The clouds were moving very slowly from the west, or a little south of it, throwing out long streamers eastwards. About 8 a.m. the threatening masses in the south-west had advanced near enough to show that at their head marched two dense and perfectly regular battalions of cloud, one behind the other, in close contact, yet not intermingling, and completely distinguished by their striking difference of colour, the first being of a uniform leaden grey, while the second was as black as the smoke of a steamer. On arriving overhead, it was seen that the front, although slightly sinuous, was perfectly straight in its general direction, and that the bands were of uniform breadth. As they rushed at a great speed under the other clouds without uniting with them, preserving their own formation unbroken, their force seemed irresistible, as if they were formed of some solid material rather than vapour. The length of these wonderful clouds could not be conjectured, as they disappeared beneath the horizon at both ends, but probably at least 50 miles of them must have been visible, as the ' Cerro ' commands a view of 20 miles of country. Their breadth was not great, as they only took a few minutes to pass overhead, and appeared to diminish from the effects

of perspective to mere lines on the horizon. At the instant
when the first band arrived, the wind—which was still
blowing, and something more than gently, from the north-
east—went round by north to south-west ; at the same time
a strong, cold blast fell from the leaden cloud, and continued
to blow till both bands had passed. From neither of them,
however, came lightning or rain, but, filling up the sky in
rear of the regular army, followed a confused rabble of
clouds, with a constant rumbling of thunder, and from which
evidently rain was falling. It was not, however, till fifteen
minutes after the passage of the two regular bands that

Fig. 46.—Cloud-wreath in Pampero.

rain fell where the observations were taken. The storm,
passing on, obscured the whole sky, wind, rain, and thunder
continuing for some hours, but only to a moderate degree.''
The diagram (Fig. 46) taken from a sketch made at the time,
represents the northerly half of the storm-clouds while
still at some distance from the spectator, and advancing
from a westerly direction.

From all this it is manifest that the changes of wind, the
rapid alterations of temperature, and the typical cloud-
wreaths are identical in character with the class of
disturbance we have described in this chapter as a line

squall. We must remember, however, that being south of the Equator, north-east, south-west, and north-west winds are equivalent to those from south-east, north-west, and south-west in the northern hemisphere.

To a somewhat similar line-squall phenomenon occurring in south and south-east Australia the name southerly burster is applied. In this case there is a sudden change of wind from about north-east to south or south-east, accompanied by a sharp fall of temperature of perhaps 30° to 40° F, during the passage of a V-shaped depression. (It has to be remembered that the point of a V in the southern hemisphere is generally directed northwards.) These storms, like the pamperos, are frequently accompanied by thunder and lightning.

THUNDERSTORMS

We have so far mentioned thunder rather as incidental to other phenomena and we must now go further into the questions of the origin of thunder and the distribution and frequency of occurrence according to season and locality. It will have been noticed, however, that an essential condition of all the thunder mentioned so far has been an atmospheric arrangement of a markedly unstable nature, either in the vertical direction or by reason of the horizontal juxtaposition of masses of air differing greatly in temperature, or more generally by a combination of these circumstances ; and that heavy rainfall and other evidences of more or less violent upward movement of the air have always been present.

The origin of the electrical conditions which lead to the discharges seen as lightning and heard as thunder has been very fully investigated by Dr. G. C. Simpson. The electrical discharge may take place between two clouds or between a cloud and the earth. Lightning is distinguished popularly as " forked " and " sheet ". Physically there is no difference, the former being simply the case where the actual path of the discharge is visible, the latter the case where the observer sees only the light reflected or partly obscured by clouds.

Many photographs of lightning discharges have been made and generally they show branches suggestive of a river and its tributaries. It is said that amongst some photographs of lightning W. J. S. Lockyer once introduced a photograph of a map of the River Amazon and its tributaries, and the last mentioned was accepted without comment as a picture of lightning. Dr. Simpson noticed the interesting feature that in nearly every case of these branched discharges the branches spread out downwards, away from the cloud.

Comparison with laboratory experiments shows that in such cases there is a downward flow of positive electricity, but some of the electricity remains in the air and does not reach the ground.

The electrical energy of a single lightning flash is tremendous ; an estimate by C. T. R. Wilson puts it at the order of 3,000 kilowatt hours.

At all times, even in fine weather, there are found to be differences of electrical potential at different heights in the atmosphere. The earth itself has a small charge of negative electricity, but it is extremely small—a current of one ampere persisting for five days could exhaust it. On the average the electrical potential rises with height, the rate of increase or " potential gradient " in fine weather being about 150 volts per metre. This potential gradient, however, fluctuates greatly in an irregular way, in addition to having more regular annual and diurnal changes. It depends to a great extent on atmospheric conditions, being low in clear air, but attaining perhaps ten times its normal value when fog prevails.

During rain, and more especially when rain falls in thunderstorms, the potential gradient undergoes remarkable fluctuations, ranging from positive values of the order of 10,000 volts per metre to negative values of the same order. Raindrops are usually electrified, either positively or negatively, but mostly positively.

N

Dr. G. C. Simpson from numerous experiments reached the conclusion in 1909 that the principal cause of the electrification of rain and of thunder clouds is the breaking up of waterdrops. When a large waterdrop falls through the air its speed may reach a point at which the drop separates into a number of small drops and these become charged with positive electricity in the process of the separation. A corresponding total of negative electricity is carried away either by the air or by the finer spray formed when the large drop breaks up. The powerful upward currents present in line squalls and under conditions of great atmospheric instability not only give rise to heavy rain but further promote the process of breaking up the falling waterdrops.

Dr. Simpson's theory is that the strong up-currents of air within an active cumulonimbus cloud produce electrical separation within the cloud, so that the cloud as a rule is positively electrified in its lower part and negatively electrified in the upper part. C. T. R. Wilson and others, however, have found that in many cases the electrification appears to be distributed in the opposite way, namely, positive above and negative below, but there is not yet agreement as to whether this is necessarily adverse to Simpson's theory. At all events the theory is supported by numerous laboratory experiments and fits in with many of the facts of observation, including in particular the rapid uprushes of humid air so fundamental in the production of thunderstorms.

DISTRIBUTION OF THUNDERSTORMS

A study of the cases in which thunderstorms have occurred has enabled the conditions to be specified as follows in the *Meteorological Glossary*. The conditions are : " First, an adequate supply of moisture for cloud development (in the British Isles always below 10,000 feet and almost always below 6,000 feet) ; secondly, a lapse rate of temperature in excess of the saturated adiabatic through a range of height of not less than 10,000 feet above the cloud base, and usually much more in the case of severe storms." These conditions are not usually fulfilled on fine summer days, however hot, in anticyclonic weather. As has been noted, shallow depressions or extensions in cols are the synoptic situations most favourable to thunderstorms.

Thunderstorms are not very frequent in the British Isles. The under-noted table, compiled from the Meteorological Office records of thirty-five years, gives the " odds against one " occurring on any particular day in the several seasons of the year.

TABLE VIII

ODDS AGAINST THE OCCURRENCE OF A THUNDERSTORM ON ANY PARTICULAR DAY

					Spring	Summer	Autumn	Winter
Scotland	N.	.	.	.	310	75	246	416
	E.	.	.	.	119	22	217	902
	W.	.	.	.	55	27	77	96
England	N.E.	.	.	.	41	13	83	475
	E.	.	.	.	33	11	64	306
	S.E.	.	.	.	42	16	62	317
	Midlands		.	.	32	12	68	507
	N.W.	.	.	.	47	21	53	156
	S.W.	.	.	.	98	49	77	204
Scilly and Channel Islands				.	63	31	47	60
Ireland	N.	.	.	.	95	36	198	206
	S.	.	.	.	72	35	119	201

This table shows that on the whole the chief risk is in summer, and that it only rises fairly high in England east, south-east, north-east, and Midlands, for which areas in summer the chances are for a thunderstorm once in about a fortnight. In Scotland east and England north-west the chances are for one in three weeks. This is as we should expect it to be, because, with the prevailing wind from some westerly point, it is in the eastern parts of the country and the Midlands that most convectional activity occurs in summer. For the same reason we expect thunderstorms to occur most frequently in the afternoons, but if a suitable degree of instability exists, and any impulse such as the passage of the cold front of a depression happens to coincide with it, then it is quite possible for thunderstorms to develop during the night or at almost any time of the day.

The table given above indicates a relatively high frequency of thunderstorms in some of the western districts in winter. This peculiarity was pointed out so long ago as 1869 by Buchan, who noted that such occurrences in Western Scotland were usually associated with deep depressions. Similar storms also occur in winter on the Norwegian coast, and they used to be known as cyclonic thunderstorms. There is, however, every reason to suppose that like other thunderstorms, these west coast winter storms are connected fundamentally with instability of the atmosphere, though it is obvious that the relatively feeble local solar radiation cannot be the initial disturbing force. Reasoning in this manner, E. V. Newnham concluded that the instability in these cases must come from the heat and water vapour imparted by the warm ocean to the lower layers of initially cold currents of air in the course of their passage across the Atlantic to the Western European coasts. By making up trajectories, that is diagrams of the course that had been followed by the air arriving at our west coasts, in many cases where winter thunderstorms had occurred, he found that the majority of the storms accompanied westerly winds which had originally been northerly winds. He showed that when a thunderstorm occurred the air had nearly always originated in high latitudes and had thereafter crossed a long stretch of relatively warm ocean. Such air is known as maritime polar air, and he found further that with such air winter thunderstorms nearly always occurred on the west coast. The final impulse leading to the thunderstorm in these cases is probably derived from the upward component introduced into the air motion on arrival at a mountainous seaboard.

Hail

Hail is often associated with thunderstorms ; the supposed method of its formation is somewhat complex. We have seen earlier in this work that an ascensional current of air is required for the production of appreciable rain. If the upward velocity of the air, as sometimes happens in cumulonimbus clouds, exceeds 8 metres per second the condensed water cannot fall through the air, but continues to be carried up with the air. By the time a level of 4 kilometres has been reached the temperature of the atmosphere is generally below freezing point, but waterdrops may form and be carried higher in what is known as super-cooled condition without actually freezing. Near the top of the cloud, however, it is supposed that pellets of soft hail are formed by a process of condensation direct from vapour to ice. Ultimately these pellets become heavy enough to fall through the ascending air current ; and in falling each pellet collects a number of the super-cooled waterdrops suspended in the air. These drops freeze on the pellet immediately, producing a layer of clear ice.

With sufficiently violent and irregular upward currents a hailstone may go up and down several times, forming successive layers of snow crystals and clear ice. Also several hailstones may become frozen together so that the aggregates may on occasion attain remarkable dimensions. The greatest weights recorded range up to just over 2 lb.

BIBLIOGRAPHY

Line Squalls and Associated Phenomena. R. G. K. Lempfert and R. Corless. Quart. Journ. Roy. Met. Soc., vol. xxxvi (1910), p. 155.

The Mechanism of a Thunderstorm. G. C. Simpson. London : Proc. Roy. Soc. A., vol. cxiv (1927).

The Present Position of Theories of the Electricity of Thunderstorms. R. A. Watson Watt. Quart. Journ. Roy. Met. Soc., vol. 57, pp. 133–142.

CHAPTER XII

GENERAL ATMOSPHERIC CIRCULATION

IN the foregoing chapters we have devoted our attention
more to the nature of the causes which produce weather at
any moment than to the sequence of weather for several
consecutive days. We have, in fact, described the working
of various physical processes and the nature of the individual
disturbances which form, as it were, the units of weather,
rather than the manner in which these components move
or follow one another.

We have already mentioned that in the temperate zones
the units of weather, such as cyclones or anticyclones, are
perpetually moving or altering their shape, and thereby
producing changes of weather ; or to put it more formally,
weather in the temperate zone is the product of the passage
of cyclones, anticyclones, or of the minor forms of isobars.
For understanding the weather of the temperate zones or
any other zone it is desirable to have some idea as to how the
wind and weather of the zone fit into the general circulation
of the atmosphere over the globe. We propose therefore
to devote this brief chapter to a sketch, on the broadest
possible lines, of the general circulation.

The ultimate cause of the general circulation is the sun's
heat, or strictly speaking, the difference in the amounts
received in different latitudes, a matter in connection with
which in Chapter VIII we have already given some numerical
values. The equatorial parts of the globe, where the sun's
rays fall nearly vertically, receive the most heat. The polar
regions where the sun's rays strike at almost glancing
incidence, even in summer receive little direct solar heat,
whilst at midwinter they receive no heat at all from the
sun, and, on the contrary, lose heat by outward radiation

during the whole twenty-four hours of each day. Thus, taking the year as a whole, we have the equatorial belt of the air receiving great heat and the polar regions losing heat, whilst the regions between occupy intermediate places. On the analogy therefore of the diurnal land and sea breezes, or of the " seasonal breathing of the continents " to which we have referred in previous chapters, it might be thought that the belt of heated air at the Equator would always be tending to expand vertically, that air would then flow off at high levels from Equator to Poles and sink at the Poles, whilst air from the Poles would flow back along the earth's surface towards the Equator ; and that this kind of thermodynamical circulation, with perhaps seasonal modification, would go on more or less continuously throughout the year. Further, since the surface of the earth is spinning round in a west-east direction, and since any point at the Equator has a much higher west-east velocity than a point near the pole, we should expect the upper current of air from Equator to Pole to take the form, not of a south wind, but of a south-westerly wind relatively to the ground below. And we should expect the surface current from Pole to Equator to take the form, not of a north wind, but of a north-easterly wind relatively to the ground below.

What actually happens is much more complex. There is actually ascent of air in equatorial regions and descent of air in polar regions, but the connection between the two seems to be maintained by additional air circulations in the intermediate regions in a manner that rather suggests the action of a train of geared wheels each one running in mesh with those on either side of it. Since the general wind circulation is related to the general pressure distribution by Buys Ballot's law, it will be convenient to describe both the wind systems and the pressure systems at the same time. We begin with the equatorial regions and proceed towards the poles.

Along the thermal equator there is a belt of nearly uniform low pressure, the oceanic parts of which are known as the

" doldrums ", much dreaded in the days of sailing ships, for in these sultry doldrums " a ship may lie for weeks on the hot smooth water, under a cloudless sky, with pitch oozing from her decks ; a region of unbearable calm, broken occasionally by violent squalls, torrential rain, and fearful lightning and thunder". This belt lies approximately along the Equator in January, as shown in Fig. 34 (p. 120), and " following the sun " moves north in July as will be seen in Fig. 35 (p. 121).

To northward and southward of this belt we have the trade wind zones with winds respectively north-east and south-east ; and beyond these again, roughly about latitudes 30° north and south lie the subtropical high pressure belts. The position of these belts also is variable. In them in January pressure rises to a maximum over the land areas in the northern hemisphere and over the oceans in the southern hemisphere. In July the run of the belt in the northern hemisphere is considerably spoilt by the great area of low pressure over the heated continent of Asia, whilst in the southern hemisphere, which is largely ocean, the belt becomes nearly continuous.

Beyond these subtropical highs again we come to the temperate regions, i.e. the zones of the barometric depressions and of mainly westerly winds ; and, finally, after crossing the " polar front " we come into the east wind zones of the polar regions.

The part played by these various zones in the general atmospheric circulation is explained somewhat as follows by Professor V. Bjerknes. Consider first the doldrums and the adjacent subtropical highs. The air from the subtropical highs moves along the earth's surface (as a north-east or south-east wind) towards the doldrums, then it ascends, assisted thermodynamically by the heating ; it returns in the higher levels towards the subtropical highs where it descends again, assisted this time by cooling due to radiation. That the descending motion is really assisted thermo-dynamically is fully proved by the fact that the temperature

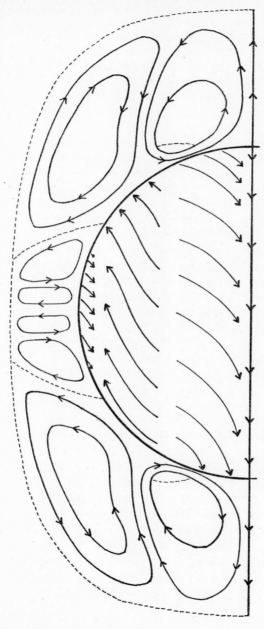

Fig. 47.—Planetary Scheme of the General Atmospheric Circulation.

at corresponding levels is lower in these highs than above the Equator.

Consider next the polar regions. In the polar east wind zone we have a similar process, tending to produce a circulation outwards from the pole at the ground, upwards at the " polar front ", polewards again in higher levels at the top of the troposphere, and finally down in the polar regions. This circulation does not attain so full a development as the corresponding one in the trade wind zones, because the thermal forces at work are not so great.

We have now described two circulations, in each of which the motion is maintained by heat energy. Between these circulations there is maintained the circulation of the temperate zones. It is an indirect cycle by which some of the energy of motion is transformed back into heat.

Thus in each hemisphere these circulations give two zones of descending motion, where very limited precipitation is to be expected, one in polar regions, the other in the sub-tropical highs ; and also two zones of ascending motion and great precipitation, the one in the doldrums and the other along the " polar front ". The reality of these various zones of low and high precipitation in itself supports the idea that, on the average, circulations of the sort supposed exist. A diagrammatic representation of the complete scheme (after Professor Bjerknes) is given in Fig. 47.

Now, as Professor Bjerknes remarks, we have no reason to attribute great stability to this system of circulations. What most affects the weather of temperate regions is that the polar front is anything but stable. The waves and irregularities in this front give rise to the succession of cyclones and anticyclones to which we have referred as the units of weather of the temperate zone. If we introduce these irregularities into the polar front we arrive at the schematic representation of Fig. 48. Moving from left to right along the polar front we see first of all four depressions in different stages of development, the first merely a slight wave in the front, the fourth a cyclone in process of being occluded.

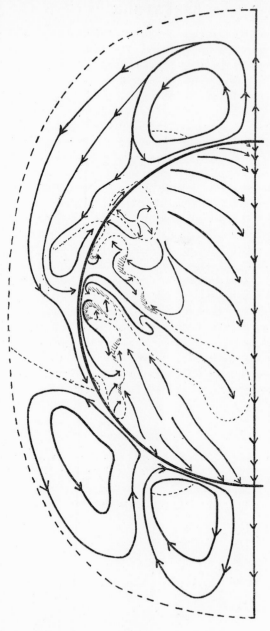

Fig. 48.—General Atmospheric Circulation.

Just to eastward of this fourth cyclone we find an example of a great burst of polar air, short-circuiting as it were the complexities of the usual connecting circulations between Pole and Equator, and proceeding in one continuous rush right into the trade wind zone. The places where these great outbreaks of polar air occur are to a large extent geographically determined. C. L. Mitchell in an investigation of the cyclones and anticyclones of the northern hemisphere finds that there are two arctic areas from which nearly all outbreaks of polar air take place. The first, to the northward of Alaska, he considers to account for the genesis of by far the most of what may be called polar anticyclones, which thus spread southward or south-eastward across North America. The second and less important locus of these polar outbursts is the area between Spitzbergen and Nova Zembla. Under favourable conditions a connection from this latter region conveying polar air direct to the tropics is sometimes formed along the western seaboard of Europe from Spitzbergen right to the North Atlantic Trades. The point of a polar tongue of this sort is sometimes cut off and left isolated, forming an independent anticyclone in some lower latitude.

Conversely the south-westerly winds of temperate latitudes sometimes penetrate far into arctic regions.

BIBLIOGRAPHY

On the Dynamics of the Circular Vortex with Applications to the Atmospheric Vortex and Wave Motions. V. Bjerknes. Oslo: Geof. Pub., vol. ii, No. 4.

The present Position of Theories of the Circulation of the Atmosphere. E. W. Barlow, Quart. Journ. Roy. Met. Soc., vol. lvii, pp. 3–12.

Chapter XIII

TYPES AND SPELLS OF WEATHER

Pressure Types in the Temperate Zone

It will be realized that what we have described in the previous chapter are average or generalized conditions, and that in this scheme the so-called temperate zone occupies a position which is likely to be characterized by great variability.

This is particularly the case so far as the western European part of the zone is concerned. Abercromby, nevertheless, in 1885 distinguished four main types of weather, which coincide with four distinct types of pressure distribution—the southerly, the westerly, the northerly, and the easterly. Since Abercromby's time the weather of the North Atlantic has been much more extensively mapped. In particular, some years after the first International Polar Year, 1882–3—a year of special circumpolar investigation in which most of the nations co-operated—it became possible to prepare a very detailed series of daily weather charts covering the North Atlantic. Speaking of these charts Sir Napier Shaw says : " I think I am expressing the experience of others as well as myself when I say that the publication of this most valuable series of charts has been destructive of any hope of simple rules for weather sequence or for the movement of high and low pressure areas. The atmosphere over the North Atlantic is shown to be throughout the year in a state of turmoil which defies simplicity of description, and it is clear that something more than a process of classification is required before the sequences will become amenable to formulated law. At the same time everybody will recognize the family likeness of the isobaric distributions which belong to Abercromby's weather types."

Earlier in Chapter XII and in Chapter VIII we referred to a seasonal tendency for high pressures to form over continental areas in winter and for low pressures to form on these areas in summer, these effects being superposed on the general distribution of atmospheric pressure. The type of weather in western Europe and the paths of depressions are controlled very largely (*a*) by the position and intensity of the nearest part of the subtropical high pressure, sometimes referred to as the Atlantic High or the Azores High, and (*b*) by the conditions over the great land mass of Europe and Asia where pressure is usually very high in winter and low in summer. In fact, as we have remarked elsewhere, the highest pressures and the lowest temperatures ever recorded are in the Siberian High in winter.

Corresponding with the various changes in these conditions we have four main types of weather :—

1. The southerly, in which an anticyclone lies over the continent to the east of Great Britain, while cyclones coming in from the Atlantic are either stopped or take a north-eastward course.

2. The westerly, in which the subtropical belt of anti-cyclones is found to the south of Great Britain, and the cyclones which are formed in the central Atlantic pass towards east or north-east.

3. The northerly, in which the Atlantic anticyclone stretches far to the west and north-west of Great Britain, roughly covering the Atlantic Ocean. In this case cyclones spring up on the north or east side, and either work round the anticyclone to the south-east, or leave it and travel rapidly towards the east.

4. The easterly, in which an apparently non-tropical anticyclone (or one disconnected with the tropical high-pressure belt) appears in the north-east of Europe, rarely extending beyond the coast-line and the highest pressure frequently being in Siberia, while the Atlantic anticyclone is occasionally totally absent from the Bay of Biscay. The cyclones then either come in from the Atlantic and pass

south-east between the Scandinavian and Atlantic anticyclones, or else, their progress being impeded, they are
arrested or deflected by the anticyclone in the north-east
of Europe. Sometimes they are formed to the south of this
anticyclone, and advance slowly towards the east, or sometimes even towards the west.

These types are so named because in the British Isles
the prevailing winds in each are from south, west, north,
and east respectively. The connection of these European
groups with those of the United States will be considered
under the details of each type.

Notice will now be directed to the details of these types—
first to their main character and seasonal modifications,
together with the indications of intensity, and then to any
signs of persistence or change of type when possible. The
specimen charts selected originally by Abercromby are
reproduced below.

But however much we study details, the above general
view of the distribution of pressure on the earth's surface
must never be forgotten, as without that we lose the only
clue to the ceaseless and complicated changes with which
we have to deal.

SOUTHERLY TYPE

In this type the Atlantic anticyclone extends very little
to the northward ; another of the tropical belt of anticyclones covers Mexico or the southern States of the
American Union ; while a third area of high pressure
covers Northern and Eastern Europe.

The North Atlantic is occupied by a persistent area of
low pressure in which cyclones are constantly being formed ;
these move up to the high European pressure, and either
die out or are repelled.

Sometimes, especially in summer, small cyclones arising
in the easterly side of the area of depression pass rapidly
near the British coasts in a north or north-east direction.

In either case it is somewhat rare for the centre of a cyclone to reach the coast-line of Europe, so that generally Great Britain is under the influence of the rim or edge of either a cyclone or an anticyclone.

At other times the Atlantic low pressure extends over Great Britain, driving the high pressure eastwards, without forming any definite cyclone. In this case the indications are for tolerably fine weather and little wind, with a very low barometer—a condition which often excites remark.

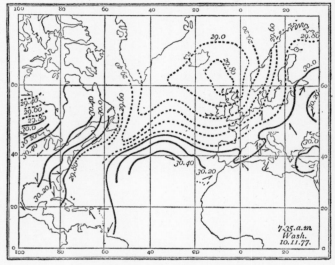

FIG. 49.—Southerly type of weather.

This type of weather occurs at all seasons of the year, but it is most common and persistent in winter; the temperature in Britain at such times depends on whether the air supply is being drawn from Europe or is coming from the Atlantic. In the former case in winter long periods of cold may result. The great frost of February, 1895, occurred in a type of this sort. France and Western Europe fairly often experience these conditions of great frost; but Britain more frequently, or at least intermittently, with the passage of secondary depressions comes under the influence of an Atlantic air supply with a relatively high temperature and rather strong winds.

No definite sequence of weather to the United States is connected with the occurrence of this type in Europe. While the Mexican anticyclone is tolerably persistent, cyclones which form in the Hudson's Bay Territory usually pass into the Atlantic and are lost there ; but at the same

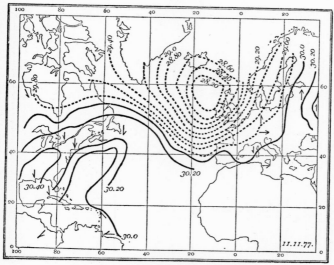

FIG. 50.—Southerly type of weather.

time another class of cyclone forms in the col which lies between the Atlantic and Mexican anticyclones, moving along the northern edge of the former and reaching Europe. The centres do not touch the American continent, but the gales associated with the western side of these cyclones often do much damage to the United States coast.

The above will be more easily understood by reference to an actual example. In Figs. 49–52 we give charts over a large area, for the four days 10th–13th November, 1877, at 7.35 a.m. Washington Time. None of these shows the zone of equatorial low pressure, but in all the tropical belt of anticyclones and the temperate and arctic zone of low pressure are very obvious. In all we find three persistent anticyclones, one over the lower Mississippi valley, another in mid-Atlantic, and a third over Moscow. The North Atlantic and Hudson's Bay Territory are covered by low pressure, and this area is the theatre of the formation of

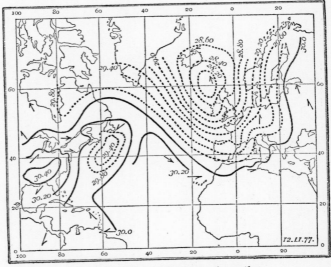

FIG. 51.—Southerly type of weather.

an incessant series of new cyclones, whose history we are now going to trace.

But first let us consider the southern edges of the tropical anticyclones. The east winds under the American high pressure are the trade winds of Cuba and the Central American republics as shown by the small arrows; the Atlantic anticyclone gives the regular trades of that ocean, and the anticyclone, whose edge we see in the chart over Moscow, really extends over the whole of Siberia, and gives the north-east monsoon to the Indian Ocean. This all shows in a very striking manner the dependence of weather types in different parts of the world on each other, and also the true nature and the complexity of the problems which the meteorologist has to solve. The cyclone which covered Great Britain on 10th November, 1877, had its origin in the Atlantic anticyclone which dominates the trade winds. Its eastward course was deflected by the Asiatic anticyclone which caused the north-east monsoon in Calcutta, and its

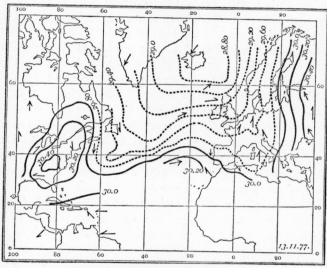

Fig. 52.—Southerly type of weather.

intensity was increased by a depression which passed into the Atlantic from the Hudson's Bay. At the same time the actual force of the wind was determined at every station by the exposure and every hill drew a little more or less rain. It is this combination of the very large with the very small which constitutes one of the great difficulties of meteorology, and all the skill of the meteorologist is required to assign to each influence its proper place and value. He cannot explain the weather on any day without casting his eyes over the whole northern hemisphere and round the little hills and valleys which bound his own horizon.

Returning now to our cyclones north of the tropical belt of anticyclones, on 10th November a well-defined cyclone lay between Scotland and Iceland, a V-depression lay in the col between the Atlantic and American anticyclones, while another cyclone covered the Hudson's Bay. Arrows show the general direction of the wind in the leading capitals and cities, and partially the varying velocity.

By next day, the 11th, the position and shape of the European cyclone had scarcely changed, but the depth had increased no less than six-tenths of an inch (20 mb.), while the position of the isobar of 30·0 in. remained the same over Europe. The Atlantic V and the Hudson's Bay cyclone have disappeared and apparently been merged into the great depression which now fills the whole North Atlantic. The nature of this change should be carefully considered, as it is most typical of Atlantic weather, and shows the nature of what the meteorologist has got to deal with, and the impossibility of formulating any simple rules as to cyclone paths. If a cyclone would only keep a tolerably regular shape, and move in even a moderately definite path, weather forecasting would be one of the most certain and definite of sciences. But when, as here, two or three cyclones gather themselves up into a new formation within twenty-four hours, there is nothing definite to trace. We cannot say how the Hudson's Bay cyclone has moved into the Atlantic, even if it is correct to say that it had done so at all. However, such is the way of cyclones, and our object here is to describe it as best we can. We often see a precisely analogous action when watching the flow of a river. The impulse of two or three small eddies seems to form one big one in a new place.

The effect of these changes on Western Europe would be to cause a rapid fall of the barometer—from surge, not from advance of a cyclone—and to increase the steepness of the gradients with the general intensity of the weather.

The irregular bends in the isobar of 30·0 in. (1,016 mb.)

over Europe should be noted, for they are due to small secondaries, and indicate rain without wind in their respective districts.

Below the cyclone-region, the Atlantic and American anticyclones are joined by an arm of high pressure, while a very pronounced depression appears over the Bermudas.

On the following day, 12th November (Fig. 51), though the position of the centre and depth of the European cyclone are still unchanged, the area of low pressure has extended over the whole of Europe, which is now covered by a mass of secondaries ; and the isobar of 30·0 in. (1,016 mb.) has been pushed a little eastwards. Observe that the line of weakness, across which the cyclone endeavours to pass, is the *col* between the Atlantic and Siberian anticyclones.

The loop in the isobars which lay over Bermuda on the previous day has now moved to the north-east and developed into a moderate cyclone, while a third depression appears over Hudson's Bay.

Now look at the last chart (Fig. 52) for 13th November, and try to say how it is related to the previous figure. The European cyclone is now represented by an irregular depression over Iceland, whose lowest point is 0·6 in. (20 mb.) above the level of the previous day, but the general sweep of the isobars unquestionably connects this with another depression in mid-Atlantic. The latter certainly represents the cyclone which lay over that region in the preceding chart, much diminished in intensity, and partially coalesced with the Hudson's Bay depression. The European secondaries of the previous day are now represented by a well-marked deflection of the isobars over the Gulf of Lyons. We can describe all this, but can we trace the history of each individual depression ?

While the weather in the Atlantic has diminished in intensity, the low pressure over Southern Europe has extended into Africa ; but in spite of all these changes, the position of the isobar of 30·0 in. (1,016 mb.) remains very stationary over the eastern shores of the Baltic.

Now, though different totally in detail, these changes are exactly analogous to the fusion of various cyclones into new configurations which occurred in the previous days, and similar changes would continue as long as this type of weather lasted. We might describe the whole roughly by saying that, while the anticyclones remained stationary, the generally low area of the North Atlantic was the theatre of the incessant formation and breaking up of cyclones.

We do not propose going into the details of the weather-sequence during this type in any one place or country, but the broad features in Western Europe to a solitary observer are very simple.

As atmospheric pressure falls, temperature rises, and the sky grows dirtier till drizzling rain sets in. The wind, from some point of south, having backed slightly, rises in velocity till the barometer has reached its lowest point. As soon as pressure begins to increase the wind veers a little and gradually falls, the air-becomes cooler, and the sky begins to clear; but the clouds rarely become hard, or form well-defined cumulus. By next day, perhaps, the same sequence is repeated, varying only in intensity, but not in general character, and this alternation perpetually lasts for weeks at a time.

The temperature of this type is mostly high, partly because of the prevailing southerly winds, and, as the cyclones die out, the slight degree of cold which follows is very noticeable. Sometimes a portion of the Russian anticyclone reaches Great Britain, and in winter white frost of short duration would ensue. The air is always damp, principally from the action of southerly winds, and for the same reason the sky is usually dull or overcast. The wind is remarkable for its steadiness, both in direction and the way of blowing. This results from the large scale on which the cyclonic action takes place.

So far for the explanation of weather after it has passed, but we may now consider how this example illustrates the nature of forecasting. Beginning in the west, the United

States forecaster has two classes of cyclones to deal with. No rules can be laid down in the abstract by which, given a cyclone to-day, he can calculate where it will be to-morrow. But by experience he knows that the cyclones which form near Bermuda run a totally different course from those which form over Hudson's Bay, and he can generally form a very fair estimate of their probable motion.

In Great Britain it is evident that when a persistent spell of this type is recognized as having set in, the general character of the weather and direction of the wind are at once indicated. The forecaster knows that the cyclones which press in from the Atlantic will never get past, so that his country will always be under the influence of the front only of the depressions. All that is necessary for storm-warnings is to watch for signs of the intensity becoming so great as to give rise to a gale. The example we have just given in Figs. 49 and 50 is very characteristic of a gale coming on entirely from increase of intensity, without any motion of a cyclone. This shows the value of any indications of increasing or decreasing intensity which can be derived from any source.

The property of any type of weather to continue for any length of time is called the " persistence " of that type. Many phases of weather are due to this principle, and for forecasting it is very important to recognize any signs of this continuance ; but, as the indications for this type are the same as for any other, we will describe the details of persistence later on.

Then as to signs of change, this type may merge insensibly either into the westerly on one side, or the easterly on the other, the latter change being usually the more abrupt ; but it is not possible to give any detailed description of symptoms of change.

WESTERLY TYPE

In this type the permanent belt of anticyclones does not extend very far north, and pressure decreases steadily from subtropical regions towards the north. Under these circumstances cyclones are developed on the north side of the Atlantic anticyclone, which roll quickly eastwards along the high-pressure belt and usually die out after they have become detached from the Atlantic anticyclone in their eastward course. Their intensity, and consequently the weather they produce, may vary almost indefinitely. When the cyclones are formed so far south that their centres cross Great Britain, and are of moderate size, the intensity is usually great, and severe well-defined storms, with sharp shifts of wind, are experienced. These occur most frequently in spring and autumn, and are the most destructive storms which traverse Great Britain.

In another modification, while the pressure is low to the north, and the isobars run nearly due east and west, the whole of the arctic area of low pressure surges southward, with an exceedingly ill-defined cyclone, bringing a rim of steep gradients along the edge of the Atlantic anticyclone, and across Great Britain, in a manner analogous to the phase of southerly type before explained. The indications then are for rain and westerly gales, with very little shift of wind. This phase belongs almost exclusively to the winter months.

But the commonest modification at every season, and that which forms about 70 per cent of European weather, is when the intensity is moderate, and the cyclone paths are so far to the north of the British Islands that the wind merely backs a point or two from the south-west as the cyclone approaches, and veers a point or two towards the west as the cyclone passes, the general direction of the wind being between south-west and west, without rising to the strength of a gale, while rain is moderate in quantity.

Sometimes in summer a prolongation of the Atlantic anticyclone covers the southern portion of Great Britain, and distant cyclones of small energy just influence the northern countries of Europe. Then the intensity is too small to develop rain, and only produces cloud in the middle of the day, so that fine, dry weather is indicated, which when very prolonged may give rise to drought. This is by far the commonest of all weather types in temperate regions, and occurs at every season of the year.

The existence of this type in Europe is sometimes associated with a similar phase of weather in the United States. That is to say, pressure being high over Mexico, cyclones form over the Rocky Mountains, and then pass

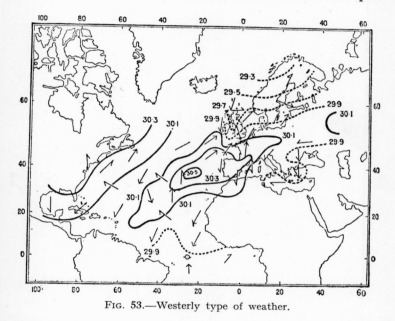

FIG. 53.—Westerly type of weather.

along the line of the Lakes into the Atlantic. To this class belong almost exclusively the cyclones which pass from the United States, over the Atlantic, into Europe. At other times a persistent anticyclone may cover the American continent, and the whole of the European system of cyclones is born and developed in mid-Atlantic.

Before we give more details, it may be well to exemplify some of the leading features of this type. In Figs. 53–6 we

therefore give charts over the North Atlantic and Europe
for the four days, 26th February to 1st March, 1865. These
may be taken to represent a fair specimen of ordinary broken
weather in Europe, without sufficient intensity to give steep
gradients and severe gales. In all, the Atlantic anticyclone
was flanked on the west by another over the American
continent, and on the east by another over Central Asia.
This last only appears in three of the charts. We have there-

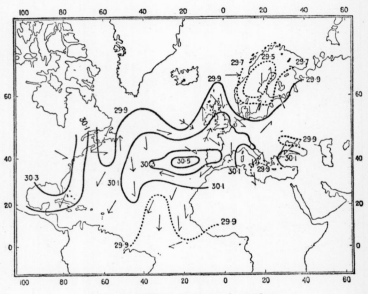

FIG. 54.—Westerly type of weather.

fore to deal with the trade-wind region south of the Atlantic
anticyclone ; the cols on either side of it ; and the slope of
decreasing pressure which extends towards the pole.

We shall take the equatorial region first, because we want
to show the nature of weather-changes in that part
of the world, but not to have to recur to the
subject. On all four days the broad features of
tropical pressure distribution are the same ; that is to say,

the type of weather is essentially constant. But in details no two days are alike, for a series of bends in the isobars denotes a succession of weather changes, some of which eventually have an influence on Europe. On the first day, 26th February (Fig. 53), the isobar of 29·9 in. (1,013 mb.) only shows one bend northwards, while the north-east and south-east trades are separated by a calm near the Equator. By next day this bend had become more pronounced, and

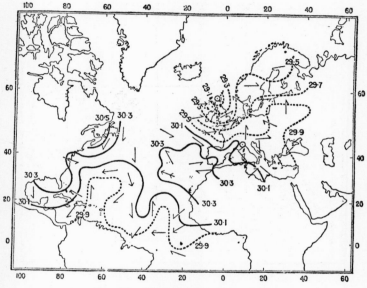

FIG. 55.—Westerly type of weather.

moved a little more to the north-east. This latter motion is very interesting, for the prevailing wind is north-easterly, but the direction of the wind has not conformed to the bend of the isobars in the manner which might have been expected.

On the third day, 28th February (Fig. 55), very great changes have occurred. Under the col which lies near Bermuda a second bend has made its appearance so as to greatly modify the trade-wind region in the West Indies ;

by next day (Fig. 56) this bend has developed into a well-defined cyclone of very moderate intensity, which moved towards the north-east, and eventually affected the coasts of Great Britain. We thus see that the details of pressure-distribution are perpetually changing in this region, but never more than a certain amount. We can therefore easily understand why the wind which is always experienced in these latitudes is described as generally easterly, variable

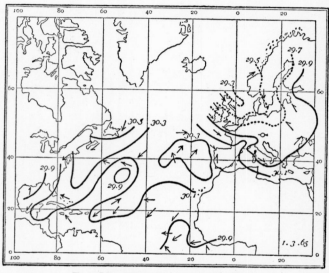

FIG. 56.—Westerly type of weather.

in strength, with the weather fine or showery according to circumstances, but not following the cyclonic sequence of the temperate zone. This modified alternation of weather is called the fluctuation of its type, as opposed to a change of type, which would involve a totally different distribution of pressure.

From this digression on the trade winds we must now return to the cyclone-traversed region of the temperate zone and the cols of the more tropical parts of the world.

On 26th February (Fig. 53) we find a part of a large cyclone over Norway, a V over Great Britain, some complex secondaries over the Mediterranean, and an anticyclone over the United States. Note, however, three innocent-looking bends on the north-west edge of the Atlantic anticyclone.

By next day the Norwegian cyclone and the British V have fused or merged into an irregular cyclone which covers Scandinavia ; while the Mediterranean secondaries have also formed a new cyclone, and a corner of the Asiatic anticyclone just appears near the Black Sea. Further west, the three bends in the isobars which looked so harmless the preceding day are now reduced to two, but have gained intensity. One lies to the south of Iceland, and the wedge which precedes it determines the weather for this day in Great Britain. The other, which is less intense, lies south of Newfoundland ; but the American anticyclone has some-what retreated.

By next day, 28th February (Fig. 55), the Norwegian cyclone had nearly died out, while the Atlantic cyclone, with its associated wedge, had travelled eastwards and much increased in intensity. In connection with this, secondaries had developed over Germany and Central Europe in the col which lay between the Atlantic and Asiatic anticyclones. Similar changes are most characteristic of European weather during the persistence of this type, and a knowledge of them is of the utmost importance in forecasting. The cyclone which has come in from the Atlantic is moving and will continue to move towards the north-east, and so far it might be said that it did not affect Central Europe ; but when we know that the passage of the depression will develop secondaries and bad weather, it is evident that the indirect influence of the Atlantic cyclone is very great. In every part of the world we may say that the passage of a cyclone in the temperate zone will develop secondaries in the tropical col over which it passes. We may also use this as an illustration of the fact that the tracking of existing cyclones plays but a small part in forecasting, as compared with the larger question of detecting influences which will make new cyclones or destroy old ones.

The col nearly over Bermuda had developed a well-marked inflection near the West Indies.

Lastly, by the morning of 1st March (Fig. 56), all these changes had somewhat developed. The British cyclone had begun to fill up, and the European secondaries had much diminished in intensity. In mid-Atlantic the bend in the isobars near Bermuda, as before mentioned, has developed into a small cyclone, which lies between the Atlantic and American anticyclones. The latter has moved a little towards the east.

We may give the general features of British weather for these four days as a sample of the type, and the reader may fill up those in any other country for himself. On the morning of the 26th, the weather in Great Britain was wet and broken from the influence of the V. Next day the weather was beautifully fine from the wedge ; the third day wet and stormy—this time from a true cyclone—and, finally, cold and fine from the rear of the same cyclone on the fourth day. Similar alternations of weather would go on, with endless modifications, so long as the type persisted. From this we see the contrast which the westerly type presents to the southerly one. In the latter, Great Britain was constantly exposed to the influence of the fronts only of cyclones ; in the former, both fronts and rears develop their characteristic weathers.

In this example the United States was constantly under the influence of a persistent anticyclone, and, so far as it goes, this shows the nature of a type of weather in that country.

We can now easily understand the following particulars of the characteristic weather of this type.

The general temperature of this type is about the average of the season—a little warmer in front of the cyclones, and a little colder in rear. In winter, however, a great prevalence

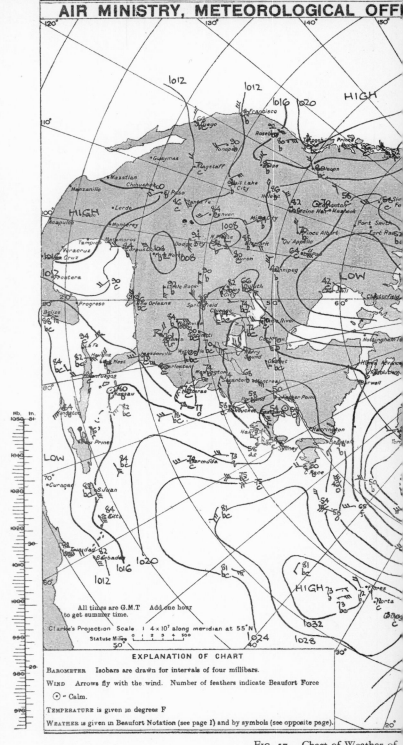

EXPLANATION OF CHART

BAROMETER   Isobars are drawn for intervals of four millibars.

WIND   Arrows fly with the wind.   Number of feathers indicate Beaufort Force

⊙ = Calm.

TEMPERATURE is given in degrees F

WEATHER is given in Beaufort Notation (see page 1) and by symbols (see opposite page).

All times are G.M.T   Add one hour
to get summer time.

Clarke's Projection   Scale   1 4 x 10⁷ along meridian at 55°N

Statute Miles

FIG. 57.   Chart of Weather of

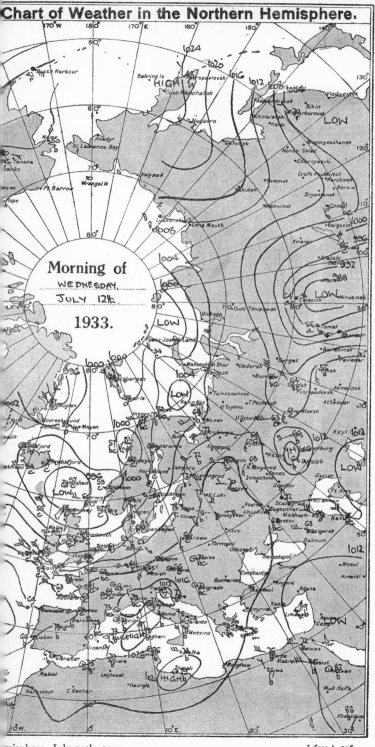

Morning of
WEDNESDAY
JULY 12th
1933.

of this type gives an open season, as the high wind prevents frost, unless the cyclones are so far north that the influence of the Atlantic anticyclone is felt.

In summer, on the contrary, if the type be intense, the temperature is below the average, from the excess of cloud hiding the sun.

Another important consideration, as regards temperature, depends on the position of the normal cyclone-path or polar front. The difference of temperature just north and south of the path is very marked, so that when cyclones pass further south than usual the temperature of the region lying between the usual and actual paths is greatly lowered.

To this type also belongs a class of warm, cloudy anti-cyclones, which seem to be associated with cyclones passing to the far north.

As regards damp, wind, and weather, the most noticeable feature of this type is the changeableness of all these elements. This must be so, because the rapidly moving cyclones bring up alternately the damp, rainy, subtropical winds and the dry, cold, polar currents of their fronts and rears respectively.

The forecaster, instead of thinking how cyclones are going to die out, as in the southerly types, has to consider along what paths they will move. This, as we saw earlier, is a problem mainly of determining the run of the isobars of the warm sector.

As an example of the westerly type in summer and also of the great development of synoptic meteorology since Abercromby's time, we produce in Fig. 57 a reduced facsimile of the Meteorological Office Chart of Weather in the Northern Hemisphere for the morning of 12th July, 1933. It will be seen that the area covered reaches the Equator in one part and extends almost to latitude 80° north in another part, whilst even the Atlantic Ocean is charted in considerable detail.

NORTHERLY TYPE

The special feature of this type is the presence of a large anticyclone over Greenland and the arctic portion of the Atlantic, which either joins the Atlantic anticyclone or is only separated from it by a col. On the east side of this, over Europe and Russia, lies a persistent area of low pressure, which is the theatre of the formation of an incessant series of cyclones, while innumerable secondaries are formed over

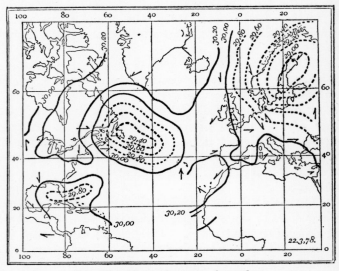

FIG. 58.—Northerly type of weather.

Great Britain and France. The cyclones either move eastwards or south-eastwards, or else, if they stand still, surge up and down and alter their shape in a very peculiar manner.

This is, in fact, the exact converse of the southerly type. In that, western Europe was persistently under the influence of southerly winds and cyclone-fronts ; in this, it is as steadily under the influence of northerly winds and cyclone-rears.

This type occurs chiefly in the winter, spring, and summer ; it is very rare in the autumn months.

On the American side of the Atlantic, this distribution of pressure exercises a profound influence on the general character of the weather. Instead of the cyclones finding an easy path into the Atlantic, their eastward progress is checked by the areas of high pressure, and in some instances their direction is even reversed.

For instance, in Figs. 58–61 we give reductions from the United States maps of the northern hemisphere for

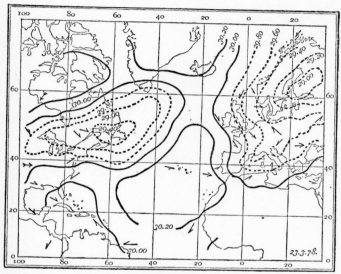

FIG. 59.—Northerly type of weather.

22nd to 25th March, 1878, at 0.43 p.m. Greenwich Time, or 7.35 a.m. Washington Time. In all, the Atlantic high pressure will be found stretching far north, till it nearly meets another anticyclone lying over Greenland ; and in all, relatively low pressure will be found both over Northern Europe and the western States of the American Union.

On 22nd March (Fig. 58) each of these low areas contains a cyclone, one over Finland, giving northerly winds and cloudy weather over Great Britain and the greater part

P

of Europe ; the other about 300 miles west of Newfoundland. An independent cyclone lies near Florida, and a col separates the Atlantic and Greenland anticyclones.

By next day (Fig. 59), though the centre of the Finland cyclone has hardly changed its position, the area has extended westwards, and the weather over Western Europe becomes rather worse.

Note particularly that the pressure has fallen about

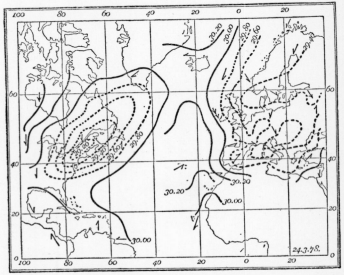

FIG. 60.—Northerly type of weather.

three-tenths of an inch in some parts of England, but owing to surge and not to the passage of a cyclone.

On the other side of the Atlantic the Newfoundland cyclone has moved westwards, joined the Florida cyclone, and so extended its area as to cover the whole of the northern states. This is the reverse of any we have seen before. The Atlantic anticyclone has enlarged, and projects further north.

By midday of the 24th (Fig. 60) the Finland cyclone has lost any definite shape, while another centre has formed over the Carpathians, and a complicated system of secondaries over Western Europe. The whole is most typical of this kind of weather.

We referred to this chart in our chapter on Squalls, for out of the complex bends in the isobars which we see over England and France developed a V-shaped depression of great intensity, a squall in which capsized the British man-of-war *Eurydice* almost within sight of port.

The American cyclone has moved towards the south-

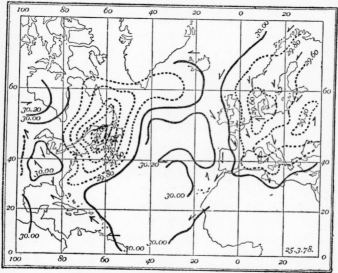

FIG. 61.—Northerly type of weather.

west and is now centred over the New England States. It has also slightly diminished in size, but increased in intensity, probably under the action of the anticyclone which lies in the north-west.

Lastly, on the chart for 25th March (Fig. 61), we see that the two centres of the European cyclone have moved as if they were revolving round each other, or round a common centre, while the whole level has risen, and the secondaries have much diminished in complexity.

With these changes, and the rise of the barometer, the weather over Great Britain and Western Europe has much improved, but the wind retains its prevailing northerly set.

Our illustration certainly represents weather-changes of exceptional complexity, but still it shows all the more forcibly the impossibility as yet of applying numerical calculations to the motions or other phenomena of a cyclone.

This is equally evident when we look on the other side of the Atlantic. The cyclone there has reversed its direction and now gone towards the north-east. Besides this, the intensity was still further increased so as to give worse weather over Canada, New Brunswick, and Nova Scotia, while one secondary projects towards Bermuda and another in the direction of Iceland.

So long as this type continues the sequence of weather at any station is tolerably simple in Great Britain. As the pressure falls the wind veers towards the north-east, with a hard, cloudy sky ; wind and rain according to the intensity, with an increase of temperature ; and then the sky clears, the wind backs by north towards the north-west, and the air gets colder as pressure begins to rise.

But during the whole continuance of this type the general northerly set of the wind and the peculiarly hard sky are never lost, and numerous secondaries will give rise to many puzzling contradictions between the movement of the barometer and the severity of the weather.

From this it is manifest that the general temperature of the type must be below the average, and the air usually dry from the prevalence of northerly winds. In spring this type frequently brings snowstorms to the northern and eastern parts of the British Isles.

During the persistence of this sequence of weather all European forecasters have to solve a problem exactly the converse of that which was presented to them by the southerly type. Then they looked westwards for the daily arrival of cyclones, and eastwards for any symptoms of a change of type. Now they look eastwards for a daily formation of new depressions, and westwards for any signs of decreasing pressure over Ireland which would be the forerunner of a different type of atmospheric circulation.

EASTERLY TYPE

In this type the sequence of weather and cyclone-motion turns round the presence of a persistent anticyclone over Scandinavia, or perhaps an extension from the Siberian anticyclone, which profoundly modifies the motion of depressions which come in from the Atlantic. The Atlantic anticyclone is, of course, always there ; but a col, which is formed between it and the Scandinavian high pressure, crosses Europe and impresses a very definite character on the weather-changes. When cyclones coming in from the Atlantic meet this col they are either arrested in their course and remain brooding over the Bay of Biscay, or else they pass through the col in a south-easterly direction. In rare cases cyclones are formed on the southern side of the Scandinavian anticyclone, with their centres over Southern Europe or the Mediterranean Sea, and these often move towards some point of west. Nothing can show more clearly than this the value of type-groups in determining the probable course of any cyclone. In the abstract, a cyclone may go in any direction, and in all the European classes we have examined above they always move towards some point of east ; but in this type of pressure-distribution only we may sometimes look for depressions which travel westwards.

This type occurs at all seasons of the year, though it is most frequent in winter and spring, and most rare in autumn. In Great Britain it often persists for two or three weeks consecutively, and gives rise to destructive easterly gales. Nearly one-half of the wrecks on the British coast are due to gales of this class. No direct connection can be traced between the occurrence of this type in Europe and any particular phase of weather in the United States or Canada.

But before we go into details we may illustrate the nature of this type by an actual example. In Figs. 62–5 we give outline charts of a considerable portion of the northern hemisphere for the four days, 25th–28th February, 1875, at about 8 a.m. Greenwich Time. In all, an area of high pressure rests over Scandinavia, while the Atlantic anticyclone reaches so far north as to suggest some features of the northerly type. The col of low pressure below these

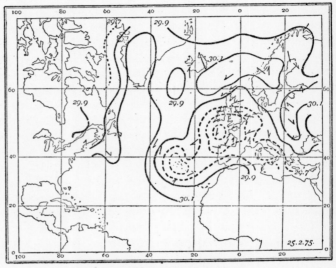

FIG. 62.—Easterly type of weather.

two anticyclones is the theatre of cyclone activity, and we shall now describe how the weather in Western Europe was affected by these changes. On the morning of 25th February (Fig. 62) we find the Scandinavian anticyclone almost meeting a wedge of high pressure stretching northwards from the Atlantic anticyclone to Greenland. The pressure for several days previous had belonged to the northerly type, with an anticyclone over Greenland, which had now drifted eastwards and joined the Scandinavian

anticyclone. To the south of this at least three cyclones
are found : one over the Azores, another at the entrance
to the English Channel, the third over Italy. These must
all be treated as belonging to the same system, as they are
all formed in the same pit of low pressure. The weather
is bad all over France, Germany, and Italy. The American
reports are meagre, but point to the existence of a cyclone
in Lower Canada.

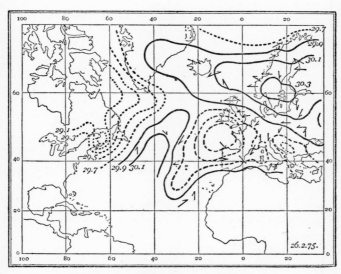

Fig. 63.—Easterly type of weather.

By next day (Fig. 63) the Scandinavian anticyclone has
increased in height, while the Atlantic one has retreated
nearly to its usual position. The Italian cyclone has moved
a little to the north-east, while that in the Bay of Biscay
has apparently moved a very little to the south-west, and
so far absorbed the Azores depression that the latter has
become degraded into a secondary. Here we have the same
fusion of cyclones which we have seen in all the other types,
combined with the stationary character which is so peculiar

to this class of weather. Across the Atlantic an intense secondary has formed over New Brunswick, while another shallow one has pushed itself into the col between the Scandinavian and Atlantic cyclones.

On 27th February (Fig. 64) these changes have made further progress. Though the general position of the European area of low pressure has not materially altered, the cyclones which lie within it have decreased in com-

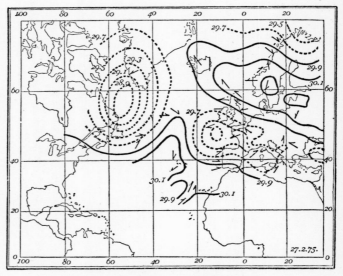

FIG. 64.—Easterly type of weather.

plexity, and a new depression has formed in a col between the Azores and the Canaries. The two American secondaries have fused into one large primary, and a large col covers the Central Atlantic.

Lastly, on the 28th (Fig. 65), while the Scandinavian anticyclone has diminished in height and area, the Atlantic anticyclone, on the contrary, has increased no less than 0·4 in. (14 mb.) in height, and much increased in size. The size and intensity of the European low pressure has diminished, but its components are more complex ; so that while weather has improved over Great Britain it is worse in many parts of France and Italy. Across the Atlantic, all we can say is that where one large cyclone appeared to be yesterday, there are now two secondaries : one intense over Nova Scotia, another slight in the Atlantic col. This is one of the cases where without charts at short intervals it is impossible to trace the exact history of the changes.

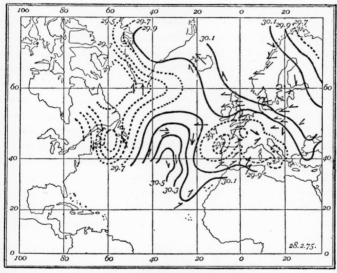

Fig. 65.—Easterly type of weather.

The general character of the weather in Great Britain during the persistence of this type is very well marked. The sky is usually dark, and, even if there is a certain amount of blue overhead, the horizon has a peculiar black, misty look, popularly known as an " eastern haze ". This is quite different from the misty horizon of a calm day in the westerly type, and is associated with the peculiar bitter feel of an east wind.

The temperature is generally low, but more variable than during the northerly type. This is because the cyclone-centres sometimes get so far east as to bring up a breath of southerly wind, which is speedily driven back by a new irruption of pressure from Scandinavia.

The wind is always from some point of east, with less tendency to back towards the north than during the continuance of the northerly type, and generally keeping between north-east and south-east. The contrast between this and the westerly type will be strikingly evident if we look back at Figs. 53–5 and note that they refer to the same three days of the year, 26th–28th February, as our last three (Figs. 63–5). By selecting these dates on different years all diurnal and seasonal variations are equalized, and the entire difference of wind and weather is solely due to difference of type.

Forecasting during the persistence of this type presents the greatest difficulties, especially in Western Europe. Though the general character of the weather-sequence may be sufficiently obvious, still there is the utmost uncertainty as to the paths of cyclones. When these come in from the Atlantic we have no means of saying whether they will pass through the col in a south-easterly direction or whether they will be deflected to a north-easterly course. In addition to this the motion of cyclones, in whatever direction, is irregular.

The signs of persistence are chiefly such as may be derived from watching the position of the Scandinavian anticyclones, and the continuance of low pressure to the west of Ireland. The signs of change, on the contrary, turn round any diminution of pressure in Sweden or the appearance of high pressure far north in the Atlantic.

The four great types of weather which we have now sketched are capable of being divided more minutely into subtypes ; other classifications have also been devised and we shall remark on these in connection with the question of persistence and frequency of types.

PERSISTENCE AND FREQUENCY OF TYPES

The word " persistence " describes that prominent feature of remaining pretty stationary which characterizes all pressure-distribution over large areas. This is always concurrent with a persistence of appropriate weather, and in this property of types we find the explanation of many phenomena of weather and of many popular prognostics.

For instance, in Great Britain an interval of cold weather in winter may be produced by the persistent influence of either the northerly or the easterly type ; or, if only for two or three days, from the wedge-shaped area of high pressure between two cyclones. So also a drought may be induced either by a persistent anticyclone, or else by cyclone-centres far north, when the intensity is slight, while long-continued rain may accompany almost any persistent type if the gradients be steep.

We mention first the explanation of some of the popular prognostics. It is a well-known saying that " When grouse come down into the farmyard it is a sign of snow ". The birds are driven down in search of food by the excess of snow already existing on the moors, and so far the prognostic would refer to the past rather than to the future ; but, by the principle of persistence, the type which has already given so much snow may be expected to continue for some time, and therefore more snow may be expected.

In Germany there is a proverb, " Fresh snow, fresh cold," which holds good for the same reason.

Similarly, the prognostics, " When a river rises without any rain having fallen, bad weather may be expected," or " Irregular tides are signs of rain ", have a significance for the future, though both are caused by past bad weather at a distance ; for the persistent type will almost certainly, sooner or later, bring more bad weather over the place of observation.

On the same principle the prognostic " Breakers in shore

without wind are a sign of storm " holds on the east coast as well as on the west, but for a different reason.

On the west coast the breakers have sometimes run on ahead of the cyclone which raised them ; but on the east coast this does not occur, as practically all cyclones move towards some point of east. Nevertheless, though the storm which raised the waves has never affected the place where they occur, still it is extremely probable that another of the same series will do so ; therefore the prognostic is good, though less certain than on the west coast.

The idea of persistence has an important bearing on fore-casts. Unfortunately, though such types are common, it is not yet possible to define any certain indications of change from one to another. One sign of persistence may, however, be mentioned which rarely fails.

Sometimes a type apparently fails for a day or two, but then is re-established with great intensity. When this occurs its continuance for a considerable time may safely be predicted. For instance, with the easterly type a small cyclone frequently passes rather far to the east, and the wind shifts to the south-west with increased warmth ; but when this dies out the easterly type is re-established in full force. In these cases the appearance of the weather is sometimes very characteristic, for, though the wind is west, the look is that of an east wind, and so obvious is this that the people say that " the east wind is not gone yet ".

C. E. P. Brooks has compared the typical charts repro-duced in this chapter with charts showing the normal distribution of pressure over the areas covered, and has drawn the following interesting conclusions. They throw some light on the question of persistence and on the changes that must occur as one type gives place to another.

In the Southerly Type pressure is much below normal over the region between Iceland and the west of Ireland, above normal over eastern Europe, and again over the Azores.

In the Westerly Type the deficit is mainly over Scandinavia, but extends to the British Isles and the excess is over the Atlantic.

In the Northerly Type the deficit is most marked over the Baltic, but affects most of Europe, whilst the excess centres over Iceland and extends to the Azores.

In the Easterly Type deficits are centred over France and over Labrador, whilst there is an excess over the Iceland–Faroes region.

There is some tendency for certain kinds of weather to recur about the same season of the year. A very complete classification of weather maps with references to the dates on which each kind occurred during the fourteen years 1905–1918 has been prepared by Lieut.-Col. E. Gold. The usefulness of this classification is that it enables any fore-caster rapidly to consult the experience of the past and to see what kind of weather has resulted on previous occasions more or less similar to any one with which he is confronted. Since twenty-eight types, however, are recognized in this classification, the application of the results must be regarded as calling for a somewhat specialized acquaintance with weather maps. In one particular direction the classification is useful, and that is where it is desired to estimate the probable developments not merely for one day ahead but for a further day or longer.

As high pressures are generally more persistent than low pressures, the positions of the main high pressure areas form the basis of most of the classifications that have been attempted. This is so with the classification, just mentioned, of Gold, and with the earlier classifications of Van Bebber and Koppen.

More recently E. V. Newnham has made a classification, which though also adopting the position of the main high pressure areas as a basis, considers the conditions over a more considerable region of the globe, namely, western Europe and the North Atlantic.

The table on p. 222 contains a summary of the results of

Newnham's classification and is intended to bring out the seasonal variation characteristic of certain types.

TABLE VII

[E. V. Newnham's Classification]

WEATHER TYPES SHOWING A CONSIDERABLE SEASONAL VARIATION

(The figures show the number of occurrences in each month during fifteen years)

Main Features of Pressure Distribution	Jan.	Feb.	Mar.	April	May	June	July	Aug.	Sept.	Oct.	Nov.	Dec.
I. Large Anticyclones .	7	1	0	0	1	0	0	0	1	0	0	1
II. High Pressure from Azores to Russia . . .	13	12	4	6	6	9	4	12	9	17	14	17
III. High over Mediterranean only	7	4	3	1	0	0	0	0	0	3	1	4
IV. Easterly Type . .	1	7	10	23	29	20	5	11	7	11	12	4
V. High in Lats. of Greenland and Azores. Lows, Labrador to N. or C. Europe . . .	6	4	22	18	20	24	13	18	6	8	20	7
VIA. High over Atlantic with extension towards Iceland	15	17	18	30	41	59	83	58	37	12	17	16
VIB. Azores and Bermuda Highs only . .	21	27	37	32	34	81	123	125	46	33	30	40
VII. Isolated European anticyclones . . .	7	11	7	5	8	2	2	4	21	20	11	14
VIII. Southerly Type British Isles and France . .	13	7	17	5	7	2	0	3	14	20	9	12
IX. High Southern Europe and Bermuda . .	3	2	2	2	0	0	3	3	15	14	6	2

In particular he finds that " over the British Isles westerly types predominate in mid winter and mid summer and north-easterly types are most frequent in late spring and early summer; in autumn there is great variability and a tendency for European anticyclones extending westwards so as to include the British Isles.

" Type V represents an unsettled type for the British Isles as a whole, and a very wet type for the northern part of the Kingdom. It is seen to be rare in winter and in early autumn. Types VIA and VIB have a very marked maximum in summer . . . the maximum for VIB is probably later than for VIA. For the western districts of the British Isles VIA is a fairer type than VIB; the figures therefore throw some light on the large mean rainfall in August over Ireland and

western England. Types VII and VIII are seen to be
autumnal, with a secondary maximum in spring, while
Type IX represents a truly autumnal type."

CYCLONE PATHS

The paths of cyclones are so important that we propose
to devote some paragraphs to their consideration, with
special reference to the bearing which they have on forecasting.

When the paths of the rare but violent revolving storms
of the tropics, which are known as hurricanes, typhoons,
or cyclones, are plotted on a chart, we find that though there
is a general similarity in their tracks there is still so much
difference that we cannot attempt to lay down any absolute
law of their motion.

For instance, the West India hurricanes usually begin with
a westward course, and then gradually bend round till they
end by moving towards the east or north-east round the
Atlantic subtropical high pressure. But in some instances
they continue in a westerly direction, and traverse the
southern portion of the United States, instead of curving
round across the Atlantic.

In the temperate zone cyclone paths are still more
irregular. A few generalizations may be made. In Chapter V
it has been stated that the direction of motion of a depression
is that of the isobars in the warm sector ; thus the typical
case has a motion towards east or north-east and a considerable majority of depressions follow this course. In all
cases the forecaster tries to determine the run of the isobars
of the warm sector if it can be observed, or, failing that, the
run of the isobars on the side where the warm sector
previously existed. One natural result of this general rule
is that during the persistence of any weather type successive
cyclones have a marked tendency to follow the same course.
Sometimes this path is entirely dictated by surrounding
pressure, but at times a coast-line seems to exercise a guiding

influence. For instance, when a small depression comes up the English Channel it often skirts the south coast of England and then moves rather more northward on coming into the North Sea. In like manner large cyclones coming in further north from the Atlantic sometimes skirt the coast of Norway.

The mean rate of movement of depressions in the British Isles varies from an average of 18 m.p.h. in May to 27 m.p.h. in December. In North America the average speeds range from 24 m.p.h. in summer to 35 m.p.h. in winter, and in Japan from 17 m.p.h. in summer to 28 m.p.h. in winter. But here again there is very great variation in individual cases.

At one time the public were fascinated by the idea that the coming of a storm might be telegraphed from the other side of the Atlantic and its arrival on the coasts of Europe foretold three or four days in advance. If cyclones only moved with tolerably uniform velocities and in uniform paths and the intensities remained constant something of this sort might be done. But from the details we have given in this chapter it will be obvious that the variations of individual cases entirely preclude the use of devices of this sort in forecasting weather.

BIBLIOGRAPHY

Aids to Forecasting : Types of Pressure Distribution, etc., 1905–1918. E. Gold. London : Meteorological Office Geoph. Mem., No. 16.
Classification of the Synoptic Charts for the North Atlantic for 1896–1910. E. V. Newnham. London : Meteorological Office Geoph. Mem., No. 26.

CHAPTER XIV

SEASONAL, ANNUAL, AND SECULAR VARIATIONS

SEASONAL MODIFICATIONS IN CYCLONES

THE term " seasonal variation " is used here in a twofold sense. In the first place it refers to the differences in the appearance of the sky or in the weather which are found at various seasons in cyclones, etc. For instance, the rear of a cyclone does not form cumulus cloud in the dry winter months of Continental Europe ; only blue sky is seen. In damp England, cumulus is formed at all seasons ; but it is much denser and more strongly marked in summer than in winter. In like manner a secondary which would develop thunder in summer in Great Britain would only produce heavy rain in winter.

Again, in winter there appears to be a considerable tendency for orographic rain to occur in the warm sectors of depressions ; this kind of rainfall does not figure so largely in summer depressions, and this arises partly from the lower wind speeds in summer and partly from the smaller difference of temperature in summer between the warm air and the land surfaces.

In the chapter on Diurnal Variation another seasonal effect was mentioned, namely, that in summer, days of tropical air have as a general rule considerably more sunshine than days of polar air, whilst in winter these conditions are reversed.

On the whole, seasonal effects such as we have mentioned are analogous to diurnal variation, for they modify rather than change the general character of the weather.

225   Q

Seasonal Occurrence of Weather

Of more importance is that form of seasonal variation which applies to the occurrence or recurrence of similar weather about the same time every year. The nature of recurrent weather in the temperate region of variable pressure may be best illustrated by looking at the connection between the variable European types and the regular annual changes which take place in the tropics. In most equatorial and tropical climates there are only two or three seasons, which correspond to two or three positions of the equatorial low pressure and subtropical belt of anticyclones. The monsoons of the Indian Ocean are the most striking and best known instances of weather that recurs at the same season of every year.

The word " monsoon " is, in fact, derived from an Arabic word meaning " season ". In the regions which lie between the tropical and temperate zones there are recurrent periods, intermediate both in their duration and the certainty of their return to the monsoons of India and the recurrent spells of European weather. One of the best known of these is the " Khamsin " (the fifty days), a hot, sandy, south-east wind to which we have already referred, which blows more or less frequently in Egypt from the end of March and through April. Again, the easterly and north-easterly types of weather which were noted in an earlier chapter as being most frequent in late spring and early summer in the British Isles are associated with the final stages of the Siberian winter high pressure system. In Chapter XIII also a table was given summarizing the types of weather showing a seasonal variation in the frequency of their occurrence.

Some remarks on the seasonal variation of rainfall in the British Isles will serve to illustrate a number of points. Just as in considering diurnal variation of rainfall we had to take account of the manner in which the rain was produced, so must we do in considering seasonal rainfall.

All over Britain the bulk of the winter rainfall is cyclonic ;

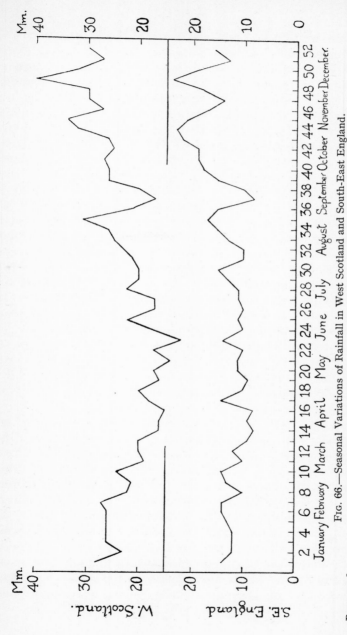

Fig. 66.—Seasonal Variations of Rainfall in West Scotland and South-East England.

in the western and northern parts of the country even the
summer rainfall is largely cyclonic ; but in the east and
south-east of the British Isles a considerable proportion,
from a third to a half of all the summer rain, may be regarded
as non-isobaric or instability rainfall, not perhaps in the
sense that an isobaric relation might not be discernible,
but rather in the sense that the instability factor plays
a large part in its occurrence. This idea is supported in an
interesting way by climatological statistics. It is known
that in the region of the British Isles cyclones are rather
more frequent and much more intense in winter than in
summer. If other things were equal we should thus expect
more rain in winter than in summer and this is, in fact,
the way things go in the west and north. In West Scotland,
for example, the normal December rainfall is about twice
the normal June rainfall. But in the east and particularly
the south-east things are different. Thus in London the
month of maximum average rainfall is October, and that of
minimum fall is April, whilst December and July have the
same amount and only a little more than June.

There must, therefore, be another factor which in its
seasonal effect works differently from the cyclonic one,
and the other factor is in the main atmospheric instability.
Fig. 66 shows the variation in rainfall throughout the year
in West Scotland and in South-East England. It is derived
from weekly statistics for a number of stations in these two
districts and covering a period of thirty-five years. The
figures along the base-line indicate the weeks reckoned from
the beginning of the year. In West Scotland the rainfall
reaches its minimum in early June—an average of 12 mm.
per week for the district—and rises to its maximum in
early December—with an average of 40 mm. per week. In
South-East England there is a smaller range of variation ;
there are two quite well-marked minima, one in spring
the other about mid-September, whilst rainfall rises fairly
high in August and is again high from the end of September
to the end of December. The August maximum is an

instability effect, the excess of rain being due mainly to thunderstorms. The high level in autumn and winter comes from cyclonic causes.

The range of variation in the rainfall of South-East England is so relatively small throughout the months that it may be asked why the ground and everything else is so much wetter in winter than in summer. The answer is that the wetness depends on the excess of rainfall in any period over and above what can be evaporated or can readily run off during that period. It is found that the evaporation from a water surface is only about 1 inch per month at mid-winter, but rises to nearly 3 inches in July, when it reaches its maximum for the year. Thus whilst the evaporation is a negligible factor at midwinter, it is usually more than sufficient in summer to dry up each month the normal fall of rain as it occurs.

In the British Isles the average amount evaporated in a year from a water surface is just over 15 inches.

WEATHER RECURRENCES

Too much importance must not be attached to the minor irregularities in the annual variation of rainfall as shown on Fig. 66 ; if averages were taken over a longer period the curve would doubtless be smoother.

In connection with irregularities of temperature so much discussion, some of it of a loose and inaccurate nature, has gathered round what are known as the " Buchan Cold Spells " that it will be desirable to mention these here. Buchan's original memoir on the subject related to the weather of Scotland in the years 1857–1866, account being taken also of certain records extending back to 1795. He found that in these years the regularity of the annual march of temperature had been as a rule subject to interruptions in the form of six cold and three hot periods. The cold periods occurred around the following days :—

7th–14th February.—The first cold spell, associated with

the northerly type of weather, during which as in the other spells, pressure was higher to the north of Scotland and lower to the south.

11th–14th April.—The second cold spell, identified by Buchan with the popular " borrowing days ".

9th–14th May.—The third cold spell. A cold spell about this time in May is the most celebrated of the cold periods, and sayings connected with it—as, for example, those relating to the " ice saints ", the festivals of St. Mamertius, St. Pancras, and St. Gervais being on 11th, 12th, and 13th May—are found in many European countries. This period is of some interest on account of the strange theories which have been propounded to explain the origin of the cold. One of the most popular has been the idea that about the middle of May the earth encountered a stream of meteors which were so numerous as to act like a cloud of dust and cut off some portion of the sun's heat. We need hardly say that such an occurrence would diminish the temperature all over the world, and that there is nothing to give countenance to this. Besides, the passage of the sun's rays through such a stone-strewed space could not fail to give rise to some kind of blur of light round its disc, as when it shines through big drops of condensed vapour. Nothing can be more certain than that this cold period is usually due to the setting in of a spell of the easterly or northerly type over Europe. At any other time of the year the same types bring similar weather.

June. — A cold spell in the second or third week is associated with the northerly type.

29th June to 4th July.—Buchan's fourth cold spell, which does not appear to figure in popular weather lore.

6th to 11th August.—The fifth cold spell.

6th to 12th November.—Buchan's sixth cold spell, associated with a northerly type of weather.

The warm periods occurred about 12th to 15th July, 12th to 15th August, and 3rd to 14th December. They do not appear to figure in popular weather lore.

These "spells" have acquired considerable notoriety, and it has sometimes been assumed that they should recur at the same dates not only in future years but in other countries. Buchan made no such claim.

From an exhaustive analysis of *Irregularities in the Annual Variation of the Temperature of London*, Brooks and Mirrlees reached the following conclusions :—

" (1) There is no apparent tendency for any of the six periods designated by Buchan as cold periods to be regularly cold in London.

" (2) There is no apparent tendency for any of the three periods designated by Buchan as warm periods to be regularly warm in London.

" (3) There appears to be a definite tendency for the summer rise of temperature to cease towards the end of July, and to give place to a period of variable temperatures which continues until the autumn fall sets in about the middle of August.

" (4) Since 1900 there has been a remarkable tendency for winter temperatures to be abnormally high, but this applies to the whole winter and not to any specific part of it.

" (5) Since 1900 there has been a general tendency for the last ten days of May to be abnormally warm, but the variations within this ten-day period have been considerable.

" (6) Neither of the last two tendencies existed between 1871 and 1900, and there is no basis for the assumption that they will continue indefinitely in the future.

" On the whole it seems improbable that there exists in our climate an abiding tendency for any part of the year to be either abnormally warm or abnormally cold for the season. It does seem, however, that such tendencies may spring up suddenly, persist for ten or twenty or thirty years and as suddenly and mysteriously vanish. Any positive conclusions as to these spells are valid only for the time and place of their occurrence, and cannot be applied to other times and places. Thus, while Buchan's cold and warm spells were probably true for Scotland in the 1860's, they are certainly not true for London in the twentieth century."

The point for the forecaster to note is that in almost every year the upward trend of the temperature in spring and early summer will be subject to a few relapses and that he must always be on the watch for the occurrence of the northerly or easterly types of weather which would bring these cold waves. In an earlier chapter we have pointed out that polar air in May or June means rather colder weather than equatorial air at midwinter. These bursts of polar air have been associated with some remarkably low temperatures in the upper air, and the latter feature sometimes provides one of the earliest and surest indications of a spell of cold, unsettled weather.

A particular year may provide some evidence of periodicity in the visitations of certain types of weather. The year 1927 may be quoted as an example of rather notable periodic recurrences and at the same time as indicating the limitations, at the present time, to any practical application of periodicities in forecasting weather. During the last months of the year 1926 and almost the first six months of 1927 there was, over the British Isles, a fairly well-defined variation of barometric pressure with a period of about a month, and associated with the variations in the distribution of pressure were certain bursts of cold air from northward, of which one, however, affected Scandinavia and missed the British Isles. This incident in itself shows the limitation to which any purely statistical or even localized consideration of periodicities must be subject. Again, just when it was thought that the above-mentioned oscillation seemed to be dying out, attention was recalled to it by the arrival of a depression and gale at a rather unusual time for gales, namely, 21st June, but, as it happened, at the date appropriate to the next minimum of pressure according to this monthly oscillation.

The idea of forecasting from weather cycles has been pursued on elaborate lines by Vercelli in Italy and

Weickmann in Germany. The former, taking a barogram covering two months, endeavours to analyse it into its component waves or periodic variations. Each component variation is then prolonged for a week into the future and the curve obtained by superposing the various components is regarded as giving the future trend of barometric pressure. The underlying idea is that the weather is governed by a complex series of pressure waves which are not permanent or invariable, but at least persist for a few weeks or months before dying away.

Weickmann works on rather different lines, making allowance for what is almost certain to be a physical fact, namely, that if the pressure waves have a physical reality, their length and rate of propagation should vary according to season.

In this country it cannot be said that any relationship has been found between solar phenomena and weather, considered over short periods. Of more importance is the possibility of a longer period connection, namely, with the sunspot period of 11·1 years, and as a discussion of it will serve to illustrate some of the difficulties of determining the extent of any such connection, we give below a short notice on the subject.

SUNSPOTS AND WEATHER

Since the middle of the eighteenth century we have more or less complete records of the relative extent of black spots on the sun's surface. These records show a recurrence of sunspot maxima at intervals averaging 11·1 years ; but the actual amount of surface covered at each maximum is very irregular, and the intervals range from nine to thirteen years. In the lower part of Fig. 67 we give a diagram which shows the relative extent, in each year, of black spots on the sun. If we were to draw over this curve another which showed the mean daily range of magnetic declination for the same year, we should find that there was an unmistakable similarity between the two curves, and that both the times and magnitudes of maxima and minima agreed wonderfully well.

In like manner a curve which showed the number of auroras observed in each year would also show a striking likeness to the curve of sunspotted area. This curve is not so valuable as that of magnetic declination, because auroras cannot be seen in cloudy weather, while magnets can always be observed. As these curves show an undoubted connection between the state of the sun and one group of physical terrestrial phenomena, there would be no inherent improbability in the existence of a relation between sunspots and weather.

Such a relation would be on quite a different footing to any quasi-astrological idea of a connection between the sun, moon, or stars, and weather-changes.

Sunspots are believed to be vortical disturbances of the sun's atmosphere. It has not been shown that individual sunspots have any direct influence on terrestrial weather phenomena, but the occurrences of large spotted areas are associated with increased solar activity and—at least up to a certain point—with increased solar radiation. There is evidence that at such times in certain tropical regions cloudiness and rainfall increase.

There is also some evidence that the depression tracks of the United States swing north near sunspot maximum and south near sunspot minimum.

Many investigators have attempted to trace some kind of connection between the amount of rainfall and sunspots ; others see a connection between the years of maximum sunspots and a frequency of cyclones in the Indian Ocean ; while some find that marine casualties and commercial panics or crises appear to follow a cycle closely corresponding to that of sunspots.

One great difficulty in deciding whether there is a real periodicity in rain or storm statistics arises from the very

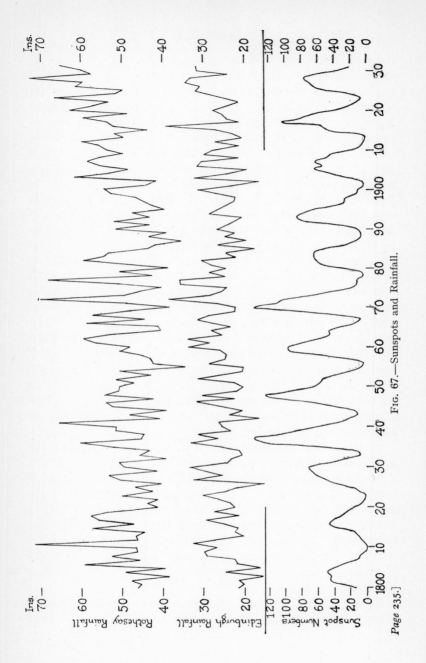

FIG. 67.—Sunspots and Rainfall.

irregular curves with which we have to deal. All the curves, on which it is sought to base the supposed connection between sunspots and weather, have as a rule been so far smoothed, that it is difficult to say what the resulting curve really signifies and how far true deductions can be made from it. This will be better realized by an example. On the upper half of Fig. 67 we have, therefore, plotted the annual amounts of rainfall at Rothesay and Edinburgh, from the year 1800, over the curve of sunspot extent in the lower portion of the diagram. Both curves are purely the result of observation and have not been smoothed in any way. The reader can, therefore, draw his own conclusion as to how far there is a real or fancied connection between the two curves. In some points there is undoubted similarity ; in others, an absolute contrariety. In the rainfall curve, if we take the absolute mathematical definition of a maximum—when any value is greater than either the preceding or succeeding ones—there is a maximum of rain nearly every other year ; but if we consider the broader sweeps of the curve we may find more resemblance. For instance, the maxima about 1805, 1816, 1828, 1837, 1848, 1860, 1871, 1883, 1893, 1906, 1928 agree passably in both curves ; on the other hand, the absolutely greatest rainfall of the nineteenth century at Rothesay occurred in 1811 almost at the epoch of minimum sunspot area ; while another very large rain maximum for Rothesay occurred again in 1841 near the epoch of minimum sunspot area.

Moreover one of the most striking features of the rainfall curves, evident despite the irregular fluctuations, is the general rise of rainfall at Rothesay during the last forty-five years, a rise which appears to have no counterpart at Edinburgh. A recent investigation by J. Crichton suggests that the rise is common to stations in the West of Scotland. It looks almost like a secular change of climate, but most probably it is a long period fluctuation which in due course will pass away ; but in any case no corresponding change appears in the sunspot curve.

In our remarks on thermograms we pointed out that because there was no obvious trace of diurnal variation of heat on many days, we were not, therefore, justified in saying that there was no such thing as a diurnal heating influence of the sun. All that could be said was that its power had been overridden by more powerful influences. In the same way the fact that there are heavy rainfalls which have no relation to the extent of sun-spotted area, does not of itself prove that there is no connection between the spots and weather. If we could be certain from any other considerations that there was a real connection between the two phenomena, all that we should be justified in saying was, that whatever connection the spots had with weather, there were other influences which might be much more powerful.

Another great difficulty which we have to face in forming our judgment of the possible connection between the state of the sun and weather, arises from the impossibility of laying down an absolute criterion of what for purposes of comparison is a rainy year. Rain may be produced by so many different causes, and the difference of amount which is measured in places near one another is so great, that we are left a great deal to our own estimate of values or probability. Thunderstorms are the great disturbers of rainfall statistics. Under those circumstances as much as two inches of rain may fall in one place, and but a few drops in another only a few miles distant. Yearly totals even show considerable discrepancies.

For example, in the year 1872 — a year of sunspot maximum—within the limited area of Scotland the rainfall near Aberdeen was 75 per cent above the average, whilst the rainfall at Cape Wrath, about a hundred miles distant, was below the average ; actually, taking the British Isles as a whole, the year 1872 was the wettest year of the past sixty years, and had 37 per cent above the normal rainfall.

Thus the first difficulty is whether to take the returns of one station more than another to compare with sunspots, when the latter affect the whole world simultaneously, or whether we should take mean values over large areas.

Another difficulty is that, as we have seen, there are different kinds of rain. The rain of cyclones may be regarded as more directly associated with the general atmospheric circulation than the rainfall due to local instability, as for instance in thunderstorms. Perhaps, therefore, we ought to reckon separately the amounts of rain due to separate causes, before comparing rainfall with sunspot statistics. We must think how the physical cause would act on the general circulation of the atmosphere and remember that the action probably takes place through the medium of cyclones and anticyclones. To establish a connection we must in fact show that in years of sunspot maxima and minima the circulation of the atmosphere is either more intense generally, or that the formation of cyclones, etc., is then in some manner modified.

This view of the true nature of solar action possibly explains some anomalies. It is found that in some places the maxima of spots are associated with the minima of rain. If we try to connect rainfall and sunspots in the abstract, we are helpless to explain the discrepancy. But if, on the contrary, we realize that an alteration in the solar heat may modify the formation or the paths of cyclones, then we can at once explain the apparent contradiction of results. For instance, in the year 1872, to which we have already alluded, the general position of cyclone centres over North-Western Europe was considerably displaced. Instead of lying to the west of Scotland, the centre of cyclone activity appeared to lie between England and Norway. This, of course, made England wetter, and the north-west of Scotland drier than usual ; but it will take many years before we are justified in saying that this displacement was due to the influence of solar spots.

It is no doubt a very tempting ideal to look at the sun as the prime mover of the atmosphere, and to endeavour to follow variations in the heat or energy of his action into their final products as wind or rain. But when we consider what the real nature of weather is, as revealed to us by means of synoptic charts, we see at once that, though undoubtedly an alteration in the sun's power would sooner or later be reflected in the results, any attempt to deduce one from the other directly is likely to lead to failure.

So far as the rainfall for any particular year is concerned, the most cursory glance at the curves of sunspots and rainfall will show that, if we were to attempt to forecast rainfall on the assumption that the amount would follow the sunspot curve, we should get just the same unsatisfactory results as if we attempted to forecast the temperature at different hours by reference to the mean diurnal variation of incoming solar radiation. Every meteorological element depends for its value on the balance of several nearly equal forces, so that an attempt to forecast the resulting value by means of the variations of one of these forces can only lead to failure.

The most striking connection that has been established so far between sunspots and terrestrial weather is that at times of maximum sunspots there is a tendency for air temperature near ground level in tropical regions to fall. Now an increase in the number of sunspots means as a rule an increase in total solar radiation so that we have the paradoxical result of increased solar radiation resulting in lower temperature in one part of the globe.

In a study of changes of climate in geological times, Dr. G. C. Simpson laid down certain conclusions, of which we may quote two as suggesting the complex manner in which changes in the sun's radiation may affect terrestrial weather. The first of these conclusions is that—

(*a*) An increase in solar radiation leads to an increase in the general circulation of the atmosphere.

Now the amount of cloud and rainfall depends on the general circulation of the atmosphere and the second conclusion is based on this idea, and is that—

(*b*) An increase in solar radiation leads to an increase

in cloud and precipitation. But an increase in cloud means that the proportion of solar radiation which reaches the ground is in turn diminished ; thus it appears likely that the actual change of temperature at ground level is considerably less than might at first sight have been supposed.

LONGER PERIODS

In addition to the sunspot cycle of about eleven years, some longer periodicities in weather have been suggested. The best known of these are Russell's cycle of nineteen years for the Southern Hemisphere and the Brückner cycle of approximately thirty-five years. It is difficult, however, to see how any of these three periods, even if they could be established with certainty, could ever be of appreciable value in seasonal forecasting because the amplitudes of the associated effects are all small compared with the random annual fluctuations.

The thirty-five-year period, known by his name, was thoroughly investigated by Dr. Eduard Brückner in a work published in 1890, but a belief in a weather cycle of this length was referred to so long ago as 1625 by Sir Francis Bacon in his essay " On Vicissitudes of Things ". From the study of meteorological records and historical records of various sorts, Brückner deduced the existence of a long series of cycles, varying in length from twenty to fifty years, and giving an average length of roughly thirty-five years— periods of relatively warm and dry years alternating with periods of cool and rainy years. He himself did not claim mathematical regularity for his cycle and according to Sir Richard Gregory " the true value of Brückner's work lies in a different direction. Although the amount of rainfall may vary widely from one year to the next, the quantity of water which is stored up on the land areas, in the soil, in lakes and glaciers, varies far more slowly. This stored water is not so closely related to the rainfall of the one preceding year, as to the average rainfall of the ten preceding years, and if these ten years fall in the wet half of a Brückner cycle, the quantity of stored water will be great. Again, in the dull rainy countries of north-west Europe, warm dry years are favourable for crops and vegetation, and on the whole the dry warm half of a Brückner cycle will yield better crops than the cool wet half, although there may be wide variations from one year to the next. An agricultural community must take the bad years with the good, and trust to the surplus from a rich harvest to tide over a year of dearth, but at the end of the warm half of the cycle the community will be prosperous, while at the end of the cold half it will be poor. Hence waves of emigration and the movements of peoples are closely related to climatic cycles such as Brückner's, which in this way may leave their mark on history. That, and not long-range forecasting, is the role of the weather cycle ".

It has been suggested that the Brückner cycle may be a composite effect of two cycles of about thirty-five and fifty years respectively, the latter of which has been more prominent in the rainfall of Great Britain in the last two centuries.

OTHER ATTEMPTS AT SEASONAL FORECASTING

Since we have mentioned the problem of seasonal forecasting in connection with the discussion of periodicities it will be well to point out that attacks on the problem by other methods show more likelihood of leading to results of value. In these matters the term " foreshadow " has been suggested as more appropriate than the term " forecast ".

In the chief method the foreshadowing is based on a consideration of the weather of several preceding seasons in the same and other parts of the world. In the pursuit of these methods, Sir Gilbert Walker and others have developed forecasting formulæ for various meteorological elements in certain parts of the world. Sir Gilbert Walker,

R

however, has suggested that the predictions so arrived at, in the case for example of monsoon rainfall, should be confined to statements of either excess or defect, and that even so the chances of success would not be sufficient to justify the issue of a prediction every year.

BIBLIOGRAPHY

The Sun's Cycle of Activity. H. W. Newton. London, Quart. Journ. Roy. Met. Soc., vol. liv, pp. 161–173.

The present Position of Seasonal Weather Forecasting. C. W. B. Normand. Quart. Journ. Roy. Met. Soc., vol. lviii, pp. 3–10.

CHAPTER XV

VISIBILITY AND FOG

UNDER favourable meteorological conditions, and in the absence of atmospheric pollution, objects can be seen at very great distances. On account of atmospheric pollution it is seldom that the industrialized parts of any country experience ideal conditions, but in such places as the west and north of Scotland and in Norway visibilities of over fifty miles are the rule rather than the exception. According to Mr. Seton Gordon the Island of St. Kilda is always visible from the Cuillin Hills of Skye, ninety-five miles distant, in very clear weather ; whilst the Paps of Jura have been seen from Hecla of South Uist, 107 miles distant, and from a point in the Cuillins ninety-two miles distant. These examples approach the limit of visibility as determined by the curvature of the earth and the heights of the objects and the points of observation, and they suggest that if objects of suitable height were available in these districts they could be seen at even greater distances. The present writer, on one occasion, on board ship between Lerwick and Aberdeen saw very clearly the tops of cumulus clouds estimated to be lying over the Norwegian coast, some 200 miles distant. The tops emerged above a line of haze just appreciably above the sea horizon, so that, allowing for an average amount of atmospheric refraction, the cloud tops would be about 20,000 feet high.

Teneriffe Peak, in the Canary Islands, is about 12,000 feet high, and has been seen from the sea 150 miles distant. Various peaks in the Himalayas, from 20,000 to 25,000 feet high, have been seen by observers from aeroplanes at a height of 5,000 feet in the neighbourhood of Peshawar, some 200 miles away.

Visibility is usually defined by the maximum distance at which an object (of size appropriate to the distance) can be seen, or the clearness with which detail can be distinguished.

Visibility is usually excellent in polar air freshly arrived from high latitudes, and perhaps for the same reason it is generally good in the rear of a cyclone or with a rising barometer. It is also good in a wedge of high pressure. In old polar air, on the other hand, in front of a depression, where pressure is falling, visibility generally deteriorates. In tropical air visibility in the British Isles is frequently only indifferent, but this is by no means always the case.

Some years ago the results of nearly 2,000 individual observations made from ships in the North Sea and reported to the Meteorological Office were classified by Mr. Charles Harding according to the synoptic situation. In such a classification it is evident that, for example, a cyclone must have included a considerable range of visibilities ; also the effects varied with season and these points must be kept in mind in interpreting the results. According to the average values, however, the mean distance of visibility in miles ranged in an anticyclone from 16·2 in May to 7·6 in December, in a wedge from 14·8 in May to 6·7 in December, in a cyclone from 9·3 in May to 5·1 in December, and in a secondary from 8·9 in May to 4·3 in August.

Though visibility to a certain extent depends on the lighting of the object viewed, the lighting of the background, and the light reflected from the atmosphere, it is limited mainly by the amount of solid or liquid particles (generally known as suspensoids) present in the air, and depends also to a slight extent upon uniformity of temperature and humidity of the atmosphere. Here we are concerned chiefly with the meteorological conditions. The suspensoids act in various ways, by cutting off the light or by scattering the light coming from the objects viewed and also on occasions by causing a certain amount of glare. The effect of non-uniformity of the atmosphere, on the other hand, is best illustrated by the shimmer often seen on looking across heated ground on a hot day. The striation of the atmosphere due to threads of heated air rising through cooler air gives stationary objects an appearance of wriggling.

When visibility is so poor that objects cannot be seen at a distance of 2 kilometres the term mist or haze is applicable ; fog is usually limited to visibility less than 1 kilometre, thick fog to cases of less than 200 metres, and dense fog to less than 50 metres.

Ordinary fogs as a rule are relatively shallow and have a fairly definite upper boundary. On land they are usually less than 1,000 feet deep and frequently less than 500 feet, whilst at sea their depth is sometimes of the order of only 100 feet. On the other hand the type of fog which is really cloud on the ground, as sometimes occurs on mountains, may be of very great thickness.

Fogs on land occur chiefly in autumn and winter and more often in the morning and evening than during the middle of the day. Sea fogs, on the other hand, especially in narrow seas, are largely phenomena of spring and early summer. In this distribution we see a suggestion of the common cause, namely, the effect of a relatively cold under-surface. In order that water vapour in the surface layers of the air may be condensed to form liquid particles the air requires to be cooled below its dew-point. This cooling may take place in various ways. A common cause is radiation on the calm, clear nights associated with anti-cyclonic conditions ; another common cause is the drift of the air over ground or sea colder than itself and yet another is the mixing of two currents of air of different temperatures.

In practically all the cases that are associated with fogs we find that the fog lies in a relatively shallow layer of cool air bounded above by an inversion of temperature. A certain limited amount of turbulence in this shallow layer appears to be an essential condition for maintaining the fog in existence. On many winter evenings, through the cooling of the air in contact with the ground, slight ground fogs form shortly after sunset and do not persist for long, the fog particles falling to the ground in an hour or two. The reason presumably in such cases is that there is a more or less continuous inversion of the lapse rate of temperature and not enough turbulence to maintain the particles in suspension.

In urban areas the existence of an inversion of temperature at a height of a few hundred feet is almost certain to lead to smoke fog in winter, because the inversion, by acting as a " convective lid ", prevents the smoke from houses and factories from becoming mixed with and being carried away in the upper air, and prevents fresh, pure air from being brought down to the ground from higher levels. In consequence the lower atmosphere remains densely polluted. In all cases calm or light wind assists in the formation of fog by giving the air in contact with the ground time to become sufficiently cooled.

According to a number of observations made in fogs with a sounding balloon at Kew Observatory by L. H. G. Dines, the average extent of the inversion of temperature at the top of a fog is at least 10° F and the maximum observed was about 17° F. A fall of temperature in the air from the ground upwards was found to be a usual but not invariable feature, i.e. there was usually no continuous inversion. The average lapse rate was as a rule less than the dry adiabatic, so that a certain amount of turbulence would be present in the fog layer.

In the course of ascents through fogs some interesting observations were made by C. H. Biddlecombe from a kite balloon at Croydon Aerodrome in December, 1924. During an ascent through 300 feet of fog nothing was visible in any direction and all sounds coming up from the ground were muffled in a way that made them appear far away. At the top, however, the observers came out into brilliant moonlight and found that noises from the ground came to them with startling clearness. In the course of a midday ascent through a similar depth of fog the same experiences were noted except that at the top there was brilliant sunshine and a very marked increase in temperature.

Some of the earliest and most important researches into the primary causes of atmospheric obscurity are those of Dr. John Aitken, of Falkirk. He showed very clearly how greatly pollution of the air by city smoke reduces the range of visibility, even many miles away from the smoke-producing areas. He also showed how to reckon the amount of impurity present in air in terms of the number of nuclei of condensation as determined by his dust-counter. A particularly interesting point noted by him is that when the wind is light and brings moist air from an impure direction, the effect of sunshine is to destroy the clearness of the air and cause a thick haze or fog. It may thus be noticed that visibility is quite frequently at its poorest about two hours after sunrise.

With the increased activity in aviation, observations of visibility become of considerable importance, and in recent years much information from stations in all parts of the country has become available. It is found that in all places there is this temporary increase of fog or haze between one and two hours after sunrise, though the tendency is most evident in districts strongly affected by atmospheric pollution. Though connected in this way with pollution, the maximum of fog or haze occurs rather earlier in the day than the maximum of atmospheric pollution.

BIBLIOGRAPHY

The Formation of Fog and Mist. G. I. Taylor. Quart. Journ. Roy. Met. Soc., vol. xliii (1917), pp. 241–268.
Fog. F. Entwistle. London : Roy. Aeron. Soc. Reprints, 28 (1928).
The Sun as a Fog Producer. John Aitken. Edin. Proc. Roy. Soc., xxxii (1912).
The Physical Conditions controlling Visibility through the Atmosphere. M. G. Bennett. Quart. Journ. Roy. Met. Soc., vol. lvi, pp. 1–29 (1930).

CHAPTER XVI

TORNADOES AND REVOLVING STORMS

INTRODUCTORY

IN dealing with the relation of wind to barometric gradient we have explained that the barometric gradient is balanced by the sum of two terms, one of which we called the geostrophic component and the other the cyclostrophic component. In cases where the air pursues a straight course the second component vanishes, but in cases where the course is a curve of small radius the second component becomes highly important. Also, the first component is one which depends on the latitude in such a way that at the Poles and in higher or temperate latitudes it is most important, whilst in lower latitudes it is very small. Thus it comes about that in the storms of low latitudes the cyclostrophic term, i.e. the one involving centrifugal force requires to be the main factor in balancing any steep barometric gradient and this can only be the case where the air describes a course of sharp curvature at a high speed, i.e. in intense storms of small diameter.

In dimensions tornadoes and hurricanes are of small area compared with the cyclones of higher latitudes, but they may be of great violence.

TORNADOES

The following description of a tornado as experienced in the United States has been given by Professor R. de Courcy Ward :—

" Briefly stated, a tornado is a very intense, progressive whirl, of small diameter, with inflowing winds which increase tremendously in velocity as they near the centre, developing there a counter-clockwise vorticular ascensional movement whose violence exceeds that of any other known storm. From the violently-agitated main cloud-mass above there usually hangs a writhing funnel-shaped cloud, swinging to and fro, rising and descending—the dreaded sign of the tornado. With a frightful roar, as of ' ten thousand freight trains ', comes the whirl, out of the dark, angry, often lurid west or south-west, advancing almost always towards the north-east with the speed of a fast train (twenty to forty miles an hour, or more) ; its wind velocities exceeding 100, 200, and probably sometimes 300 or more miles an hour ; its path of destruction usually less than a quarter of a mile wide ; its total life a matter of perhaps an hour or so. It is as ephemeral as it is intense. In semi-darkness, accompanied or closely followed by heavy rain, usually with lightning and thunder, and perhaps hail, the tornado does its terrible work. Almost in an instant all is over. The hopeless wreck of human buildings, the dead, and the injured, lie on the ground in a wild tangle of confusion. The tornado has passed by.

" Fortunately for man, tornadoes are short-lived, have a very narrow path of destruction, and are by no means equally intense throughout their course. Their writhing funnel cloud, which indicates the region of maximum velocity of the whirling winds, ascends and descends irregularly. Sometimes it may be seen travelling along with its lower end at a considerable distance aloft, like a great balloon. The tornado is then in the clouds, its natural home. Again, under other conditions, the funnel cloud works its way downward to the earth, like a huge gimlet, its base enlarged by the debris drawn in by the inflowing winds ; its violence so intense that nothing can resist it. Where the funnel cloud descends, the destruction is greatest ; where it rises there are zones of greater safety. The whirl may be so far above the ground that it does no injury whatever. It may descend low enough to tear roofs and chimneys to pieces. It may come down to the ground and leave nothing standing. . . .

"We may thus roughly classify the damage done by tornadoes as follows : (1) That resulting from the violence of the surface winds blowing over buildings and other exposed objects, crushing them, dashing them against each other, etc. ; (2) that caused by the explosive action ; and (3) that resulting from the uprushing air movement close around the central vortex. Carts, barn-doors, cattle, iron chains, human beings, are carried through the air, whirled aloft, and dashed to the ground, or they are dropped gently at considerable distances from the places where they were picked up. A horse has been carried alive for over two miles. Iron bridges have been removed from their foundations. A cart weighing 600 lb. has been carried up in a tornado, torn to pieces, and the tyre of one wheel was found 1,300 yards away. Beams are driven into the ground, nails are forced head-first into boards ; cornstalks are driven partly through doors. Harness is stripped from horses : clothing is torn from human beings and stripped into rags. In one place the destruction may be complete, with every building and tree and fence levelled to the ground. A few feet away the lightest object may be wholly undisturbed. The damage is greater, and extends farther from the centre, on the right of the track than on the left, for the wind velocities are greater on the right, as in the ' dangerous semi-circle ' on the right of the track of tropical cyclones.

"The explosive effects are many and curious. The walls of buildings—one or more of them—fall out, sometimes letting the roof collapse on to the foundations ; or the roof may be blown off, leaving the walls standing."

Even in the British Isles tornadoes are not unknown, though their degree of violence is much less. On 27th October, 1913, a storm of this type moved from South Devon to Cheshire. In South Wales it left a narrow track of destruction from 50 to 300 yards wide and 12 miles long, within which houses and factories were wrecked and five people were killed.   The rate of advance of the tornado was about thirty-five miles per hour.   In 1925 a similar tornado caused considerable damage in Holland.

Again in 1931 visitations of a similar sort occurred in England on 14th June and in Westphalia on 17th June. The tornado of 14th June passed in a north-easterly direction

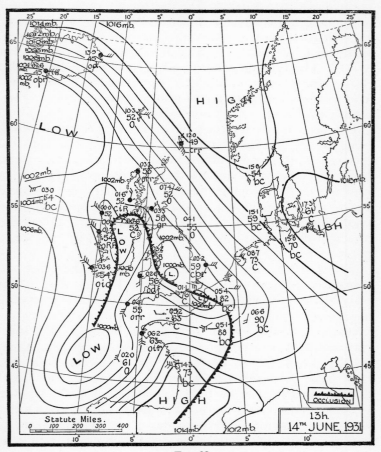

FIG. 68.

across Birmingham at a speed of about thirty miles an hour, the track within which the structural damage occurred being from 200 to 800 yards in width and 10 to 12 miles in length. In an examination of these two cases W. H. Pick found each to be associated with the passage of the line of occlusion of a depression. Fig. 68 shows the synoptic chart for 13 h. of 14th June, when a complex series of small depressions covered the British Isles. The part of the occlusion shown as running from northern Ireland to southern England on this chart moved rapidly north-eastward, and at 18 h. occupied a position extending from the Hebrides to the Wash. The tornado occurred at Birmingham about 15 h. during the passage of this line of occlusion. The South Wales tornado of 1913 seems also to have occurred along a well-defined line of occlusion.

Fig. 69 is taken from a photograph of a tornado which occurred at Peshawar on 5th April, 1933, during the passage of a depression across north-west India. According to R. G. Veryard it appears that the phenomenon in this case was the result of vigorous convection between relatively strong and superadjacent air currents of different directions and different origins. The photograph was taken by Mr. Russell Pleasants and is reproduced with his kind permission.

Whilst there is no exact knowledge as to the origin of tornadoes it seems probable that they always arise as an eddy between two masses of air moving in opposite directions and these conditions are frequently found along a line of occlusion. A. Wegener in 1917 developed the theory that the vital part of a tornado is a vortex with horizontal axis, usually directed from north-west to south-east, with the right-hand or south-easterly end of the vortex prolonged at times and bent down to the ground. Sir G. T. Walker in 1929 further developed this theory. He noted particularly that in the South Wales tornado of 27th October, 1913, and in other continental cases, " the heaviest rain fell 20 to 30 miles to the left of the shown track, with patches

[*face p.* 252

Fig. 69.   Tornado at Peshawar, April 5th, 1933.

of exceptional heaviness opposite three or four places where the tornado was exceptionally violent," also that articles picked up and carried for considerable distances are generally transported in a direction between north-east and north-west of their starting point, whilst objects carried only very short distances may go in any direction. He considers that the vortex tends to set itself parallel to the earth's axis and that the circumstance of the right-hand end of the eddy being inclined to the ground gives much better conditions for the updraught of air leading to heavy rain and hail and winds with strong ascending components.

TROPICAL REVOLVING STORMS

The revolving storms of tropical regions are of greater dimensions but less violence than tornadoes. They are known as hurricanes in the West Indies and the South Pacific, whilst in the North-West Pacific and China Sea they go by the name of typhoons and in the Indian Ocean by the name of cyclones. They appear first as a rule some 5° to the northward or southward of the Equator and usually follow curved paths, first moving westward, then bending away from the Equator, and finally moving towards north-east in the northern hemisphere and towards south-east in the southern hemisphere. In some cases it would appear that hurricanes have travelled round the western end of the Atlantic subtropical high pressure area, over the West Indies, and finally eastward across the Atlantic to reach the British Isles as quite ordinary depressions.

The rate of motion of these tropical storms is usually less than 10 miles per hour. The circular area covered may be only some 20 miles in diameter or may reach some hundreds. On the whole the greatest frequency of occurrence is in late summer, though they may be experienced in almost any month.

The hurricanes of the West Indies occur most frequently from June to November, the hurricanes of the North Pacific and the typhoons of the China Seas from July to October, and the cyclones of the Arabian Sea and Bay of Bengal from April to December or January. In the southern hemisphere the months of greatest frequency are November to April for the hurricanes of the South Pacific and October to July for the cyclones of the South Indian Ocean.

To a ship at sea the first sign of an approaching storm is frequently the swell. The effect of the violent winds blowing in the direction of advance of the system is to develop great sea waves which travel to great distances and at a speed greater than the comparatively slow rate of advance of the storm centre. The swell so formed may often be noted 200 to 500 miles from the centre, and may thus sometimes give a warning at a place one or two days in advance of the arrival of the centre.

Cirrus clouds appearing to diverge from a point on the horizon may also indicate the direction of a tropical storm ; remarkable sky colourings, red or copper at sunset and sunrise are other frequent premonitory signs.

In the matter of barometric pressure any departure from the regular semi-diurnal variation which in tropical regions is so conspicuous a feature of most days, is to be regarded with suspicion.

Wind speeds of 100 miles per hour may be reached in tropical storms, but the zone of violent winds may be quite narrow. Thus the American S.S. *Eclipse* in December, 1922, encountered in the Arabian Sea a cyclone in which the ring of winds of hurricane force was estimated to be only 4 miles thick, whilst the relatively calm centre was only 4 miles in diameter.

Again, Rear-Admiral H. P. Douglas, in H.M.S. *Mutine*, in September, 1922, in the West Indies, observed a case where the ring of winds of hurricane force was 15 miles thick in advance of the centre and 19 miles thick in the rear, whilst the central zone was about 7 miles in diameter. According to *The Marine Observer* this particular hurricane originated in the tropics, recurved in about lat. 25° N., long. 66° W., then crossed the Atlantic and reached the French coast as a large depression some four days later. By this time the system had so increased in area that its diameter was about 1,000 miles ; some ships reported winds of hurricane force near the centre.

The relatively small area of winds of hurricane force in these tropical storms, coupled with increasing knowledge about them and the information which ships on occasions may pass to one another by wireless telegraphy, renders it practicable nowadays for ships as a rule to avoid some at least of the worst dangers of hurricanes.

Remarkably low barometric pressures have been recorded from time to time in tropical revolving storms. The lowest known is a reading of 886·8 mb. (26·185 in.) on 18th August, 1927, on the Dutch steamship *Sapaeraea* in the Pacific Ocean, 460 miles east of the Philippines. It is possible that still lower pressures occur in the centres of tornadoes, but no exact records exist.

WHIRLWINDS, WATERSPOUTS, HABOOBS

These phenomena are rotational storms on a smaller scale. Small whirlwinds may sometimes be seen on hot days, especially in dry countries. Waterspouts are less frequently observed, but are not unknown even in the seas around the British Isles.

The haboobs of dry, sandy countries look like an advancing wall of dust and sand when seen from a distance ; the " wall " may be as much as 15 kilometres in length and 2 kilometres in height. Closer examination shows it to be apparently of buttressed character, the " buttresses " being in reality so many whirling columns of air and sand, so that to this extent a haboob may be regarded as a collection of small whirlwinds. It is considered that haboobs arise mainly from a current of cold air undercutting warm air. Like many other instability phenomena they have a pronounced diurnal variation, being commonest in late afternoon and early evening.

RELATION OF TORNADOES AND REVOLVING STORMS TO CYCLONES

Before concluding this chapter, we may make a few remarks on an interesting question which here presents itself. Commencing with a whirlwind only two or three feet across, we find revolving storms of every gradation of size till we come to the destructive tornado, and the tropical revolving storm. Also, from the small secondary which deflects the wind in connection with a thunderstorm, there seems to be every gradation of size into the secondary, which is so large that we can hardly say whether it should not be called a primary cyclone. Is there a connection between the two series ?

In both the whirlwind and cyclone series we have certain common features—a horizontal rotation, and more or less uptake near the centre of the gyration. Also both tornadoes and cyclones appear to be associated with surfaces of discontinuity of the atmospheric circulation. We can say at once too that in the cyclonic depression series the centrifugal effects play a less obvious part in the determination of the wind circulation ; but cyclonic disturbances, even if unsymmetrical in their initial stages, also tend eventually towards symmetry about a centre. Moreover, as we have mentioned, cases have been known where a revolving storm apparently has crossed the Atlantic to appear on this side as an ordinary depression.

The apparent absence of transitional forms is somewhat remarkable and leads us to return to a problem mentioned in the chapter on the Structure of Cyclones, namely, whether a cyclone at any stage can be regarded as containing within it a core or disc of air rotating like a solid. The remarks made in that chapter related to the surface air which for one reason and another is more or less incurved to the isobars. Here we set aside surface effects for the moment and consider the circulation in the cyclone as a whole, after the manner adopted by Sir Napier Shaw.

Let us suppose that there is actually a great disc of air rotating like a solid with angular velocity ζ say, in the cyclonic direction, about a centre O, the centre travelling from west to east with velocity V. We wish to examine how the air movement would appear in the instantaneous bird's-eye view offered to us by a synoptic chart.

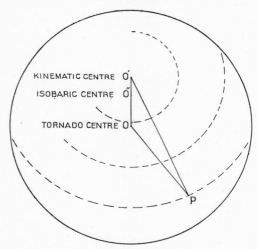

KINEMATIC CENTRE O'
ISOBARIC CENTRE O''
TORNADO CENTRE O
P

FIG. 70.—Combination of translation and rotation.

The movement of the air at a point P (Fig. 70) is compounded of the eastward translational movement V of the centre, and the rotational movement $OP \cdot \zeta$ perpendicular to the line OP.

It is shown in books on dynamics that the resultant instantaneous movement is equivalent to a rotational movement with angular velocity ζ about another point O' situated to northward of the centre of the disc at a distance $OO' = \dfrac{V}{\zeta}$. This point O', momentarily fixed, is called the centre of instantaneous rotation. The problem is similar to that of a cart-wheel rolling on the ground. The point where the wheel touches the ground is for the moment stationary and the whole wheel rotates about that point. The hub of the wheel moves at the same speed as the vehicle, and the highest point of the wheel moves at twice the speed of the vehicle.

The velocity of the point P in our problem is equal to $O'P \cdot \zeta$ and the direction is perpendicular to $O'P$.

The instantaneous centre of rotation changes from moment to moment, always moving eastward in parallel with the centre of the disc.

Thus if the winds on a synoptic chart seem to rotate about a centre, this centre is to be identified with the point O'. If there is any rotating disc of air its centre O is not readily identifiable on the chart. We see, however, that we ought to look for it, not at the instantaneous wind centre, but at a distance $O'O$ to southward, such that $O'O = \dfrac{V}{\zeta}$, and where in fact the wind speed will be V.

To these two centres, Sir Napier Shaw has given the names kinematic or cyclone centre and tornado centre.

We can see now that in the case of a tropical revolving storm, where the rotational speed ζ is high and the translational speed V is small, the distance OO' will be very small, i.e. the kinematic centre and the tornado centre will be virtually the same thing. In the case, however, of the extensive depressions of temperate latitudes V is relatively large and ζ is small, so that the distance OO' may be very considerable ; thus any solid rotation, if present, will be much more difficult to detect.

We are not yet, however, at the end of the matter for we have not yet mentioned the isobars ; actually there is a third centre, the isobaric one which ordinarily we think of as the centre of the cyclone. To it Sir Napier Shaw gives the name " dynamic centre ". The dynamic centre O'' lies between the two other centres. The determination of its position involves considerations of barometric gradient and it can be shown that the distance $O'\,O'' = \dfrac{V}{(2\omega \sin\phi + \zeta)}$.

When all these considerations are taken into account and allowance made for incurvature of the surface air it becomes possible to examine the problem mentioned at the beginning of this section.   It is found that some cases exist where the air motion in secondaries or depressions does seem to approximate to the conception of a travelling and rotating disc.   We see, therefore, that there may be a connection, at least at certain stages in their development, between the extensive depressions of temperate latitudes and the small but violent revolving storms.   The complete elucidation of the problem, however, calls still for considerable investigation.

BIBLIOGRAPHY

Hurricanes and Tropical Revolving Storms. Mrs. E. V. Newnham. London : Meteorological Office Geoph. Mem., No. 19.
On the Mechanism of Tornadoes. Sir Gilbert Walker. Quart. Journ. Roy. Met. Soc., vol. lvi, pp. 59–66 (1930).

Chapter XVII

PRACTICAL APPLICATIONS

International Organization

From the nature of the thing, synoptic meteorology is the work of an organization. It is one of the functions of the Meteorological Office in this country to maintain a network of observing stations from which brief coded reports are sent by telegraph, generally at 1 h., 7 h., 13 h., and 18 h. G.M.T. each day to the central office in London. Fig. 26 of Chapter V will serve to indicate the positions of the principal reporting stations which thus provide the data for the preparation of the synoptic charts. In all the chief countries similar organizations exist and according to an international arrangement each country broadcasts by radio-telegraphy three or four times daily a collective message, again in code, containing the latest observations available from its network of stations. The reader who wishes to have details of the codes used, the times at which the collective reports are issued, and the conditions of issue will find the complete information in an official booklet entitled *M.O. 252—Wireless Weather Messages—Particulars of Meteorological Reports issued by Wireless Telegraphy and Wireless Telephony in Great Britain, Gibraltar, Malta, Middle East, and Iraq,* price one shilling and sixpence. The booklet contains also particulars of the spoken forecasts and gale warnings issued through the courtesy of the Automobile Association and the British Broadcasting Corporation. Similar information in respect of other countries in Europe is obtainable from Publication No. 9 of the International Meteorological Organization, *Les Messages Synoptiques du Temps.*

For the purpose of the exchange of information between

different countries five principal meteorological transmissions are made two or more times daily, viz. from Annapolis (for North America), from Rugby (for Europe and parts of Asia), from Paris (for Western Europe), from Berlin and Königswüsterhausen (for Central Europe), and from Moscow (for the U.S.S.R. in Europe and Asia). The booklet (*M.O. 252*) states that " These five principal transmissions were designed mainly for the use of the meteorological services of the countries in the northern hemisphere. The reception of all these messages is long and arduous.

" It is generally possible, however, for anyone in this country to construct a fairly detailed weather chart for North-West Europe and the Eastern North Atlantic, for observation hours 0700 G.M.T. and 1300 G.M.T. by receiving the ' synoptic ' issues for the British Isles and the ' collective ' issues for stations on the Continent, all of which are transmitted by the Air Ministry Station (GFA). Less detailed maps for a larger area, for observation hours 0700 and 1800 G.M.T. may be constructed by receiving the Rugby (GBR) transmissions only. Modest receiving apparatus is sufficient for these purposes, but commercial broadcast receivers are generally unsuitable, because they cannot usually be tuned to the required wave-lengths, viz. 4,098 metres in the case of Air Ministry (GFA) and 18,740 in the case of Rugby (GBR).

" The spoken reports and forecasts issued by the Automobile Association from their station at Heston (Middlesex) are transmitted on a wave-length of 833 metres. This wavelength is just below the lowest wave-length to which the so-called ' long-wave ' band of most ordinary broadcast receivers can be tuned. The messages issued by the B.B.C. are, of course, receivable by ordinary broadcast receivers."

The information is rendered more complete by reason of the fact that a number of selected ships are equipped with meteorological instruments and transmit reports from the parts of the ocean which they happen to be traversing at stated times of the day. In this way the synoptic arrangements cover a large part of the northern hemisphere, and it is possible for any suitably equipped body to pick up information and chart the weather of a very extended area.

With the assistance of the synoptic charts forecasts of weather are prepared and issued from the Forecast Division of the British Meteorological Office several times daily. These forecasts reach the public for the most part through the medium of the daily newspapers or the bulletins of the British Broadcasting Corporation. The issues by wireless telegraphy have the advantage that they arrive without appreciable delay, whilst the reports appearing, for example in morning newspapers, are forecasts made on the previous evening on the basis of the 18 h. observations. In several newspapers, however, a daily synoptic chart is also published and though on rather a small scale it conveys, to those familiar with such charts, a rather fuller idea than can be given in words as to the general weather situation.

A printed Daily Weather Report is also issued by the Meteorological Office. It comprises three sections, as follows :—

(a) The British Section, ready about 12.30 p.m., contains in detail the observations made at the reporting stations in our Islands, at 13 h. and 18 h. of the previous day and at 1 h. and 7 h. of the day of issue, together with evening and morning observations from five capital cities on the Continent. It contains also a synoptic chart for 7 a.m. covering the British Isles and the adjacent parts of the Continent, together with the official forecasts ; also a chart on a smaller scale and compiled from observations not strictly synchronous, of the weather of the northern hemisphere. Fig. 57 (Chapter XIII) is an example of the last-mentioned chart.

(b) The International Section, issued about 3.30 p.m., contains synoptic charts for 7 h. of the day of issue and 18 h. of the previous day, covering Europe, the Mediterranean, and the Eastern Atlantic ; also charts of a smaller area for 13 h. and 1 h., and a table of observations taken at about eighty stations, mostly on the Continent of Europe.

FIG. 71.—British Forecast Districts.

This section is useful to anyone wishing to trace the course of various weather systems in detail.

(c) The Upper Air Section contains maps, diagrams, and tables showing upper air currents and upper air temperatures over the British Isles and on the Continent of Europe.

Ordinarily the official forecast consists of three parts : (a) The " general inference " drawn from the chart, (b) the district forecasts for twenty-four hours from the time of issue of the statement, and (c) a "further outlook" generally for a further period of twenty-four hours.

The " districts " into which the British Isles are regarded as being divided for the purposes of forecasts are indicated on the map in Fig. 71.

It will be evident that any one of these districts is small compared with the area covered by an ordinary cyclone or other isobaric type. The need for a division into districts arises from the considerations set out in the chapter on Local Variation of Weather ; and the general principle on which the division is made is that so far as possible a district should be an area all parts of which are likely as a rule to be similarly affected by any given type of weather. But even when the country has been divided into twenty-one districts, the forecaster, on occasions finds himself obliged to distinguish between the inland and coastal parts, or the high and low ground of a district. It may blow a gale at Dover and only a fresh breeze in London. On the other hand it is generally possible to group the districts in some way, though not always in the same way, and so to limit the number of separate statements of probable weather.

Great Britain is situated in a region of peculiar difficulty. Not only does her insular position limit the detail of the information available from the great area to westward from which most disturbances come, but she is more exposed to variable and unsettled weather than other parts of Europe. As we have noted in the chapter on Types and Spells of Weather, Britain is frequently situated just on the boundary between a cyclonic and an anticyclonic system or between mild, humid conditions and cold, dry conditions. Obviously even slight displacements in the general situations, if not accurately foreseen, can upset the calculations of the weather forecaster.

GALE WARNINGS FOR SHIPPING

About seventy years have now elapsed since the inauguration in this country of a system of gale warnings. The system provides for the issue by the Meteorological Office of notices of the probability of gales or high winds, the notices being sent by telegram to ports and fishing stations around the coasts of our islands. The fact that one of these notices has been received at any station is made known by day by the hoisting of a black canvas cone, 3 feet high and 3 feet wide at the base. By night a signal consisting of three lanterns hung on a triangular frame is employed at some stations. An official note states that—

" The North Cone (point upwards) is hoisted for gales commencing from a northerly point.

" For gales commencing from east or west the North Cone will be hoisted if the gale is expected to change to a northerly direction.

" The South Cone (point downwards) is hoisted for gales commencing from a southerly point. Such gales often veer, sometimes as far as north-west.

" For gales commencing from east or west the South Cone will be hoisted if the gale is expected to change to a southerly direction."

When these warnings are issued to the coastal stations, they are also broadcast from certain wireless stations so that ships approaching the British Isles from any direction may receive notice of any gale anticipated. The measure of success attending the issue of gale warnings is indicated by the fact that in recent years about 80 per cent of all warnings issued have been followed by gales or high winds within the areas warned, whilst effective warnings were issued for about 92 per cent of the gales experienced. As bearing on the difference between the two percentages just quoted it has to be kept in mind that whilst the forecaster will not wish to issue an unjustified warning if it can be avoided, still less may he take the risk of withholding a warning in cases of doubt.

REPORTS AND FORECASTS FOR AVIATION

In aviation weather is vital, and meteorological stations are now attached to the principal aerodromes, whilst special weather-reporting services are in operation on all important air routes. The contact of the official meteorological services with the aviator is a much closer one than the contact with the general public. The aviator presents his inquiry direct and in concise form. He wishes to know not only the wind and the general weather conditions, but more particularly to have detail in regard to those factors which affect the safety or the possibility of his intended flight, namely, the visibility and the height of the lowest cloud ; and for the most part he is interested in a very short period—a few hours. Fortunately it is possible to forecast with considerable accuracy in these matters for brief periods ahead.

AGRICULTURE AND INDUSTRY

The farmer as a rule asks two things of the forecaster, namely, notice in advance of spells of fine weather, and warning of the various forms of bad weather which may cause him loss. The first kind of notice can usually only be issued when it is recognized that a spell of settled anticyclonic weather has set in. Occasionally, however, the weather remains surprisingly fine for appreciable periods in unsettled conditions when, owing to the liability to sudden change, the issue of a notice would not be justified.

In regard to bad weather, the phenomena to be feared vary according to the climate and the type of farming. Thus in fruit-growing countries spring frosts or hail may bring disaster. With adequate warning it is sometimes practicable to arrange protective measures against frosts ; but protection against hailstorms is scarcely practicable, and the wise grower safeguards himself where possible by insurance.

In sheep-farming areas warning of snowstorms, particularly in the lambing season, is valuable provided the warning can be issued in time to enable flocks to be collected from exposed areas.

In the British Isles notifications of fine spells and warnings of snowstorms are added, as occasion justifies, to the forecasts issued by the British Broadcasting Corporation.

The requirements and problems of industry vary so widely that individual attention must as a rule be given to each case. Visibility and fog, ice and snow bulk largely in the operation of all forms of transport, whilst weather in a general way, and particularly anticipated weather, considerably affects the number of passengers to be provided for in certain cases. Climatic conditions affect not only certain manufacturing processes but also the sales of certain products.

FLOODING

Particular districts may be open to the risk of flooding arising from heavy rainfall or the thawing of snow or as a result of tides amplified by weather conditions.

Disastrous flooding is generally associated with a combination of various factors, for example, exceptionally heavy rain resulting first in swollen rivers, then the blocking of a river bed by debris, and finally the sudden release of a vast accumulation of water carrying devastation to the country lower down the course of the river.

Alternatively, in the case of a narrow tidal estuary, if the peak of the run-off following exceptional rainfall in the river basin happens to coincide with an unusually high tide in the estuary, the surrounding country may be liable to temporary flooding. Even without unusual rainfall cases of this sort have occurred in the British Isles, and the disastrous Thames flood of 6th to 7th January, 1928, may be mentioned as illustrating one type of these events. Following on this particular flood an investigation (by A. T. Doodson and J. S. Dines) showed that there was some complication in regard to the causes. In regard to the meteorological conditions it was found that a pressure distribution giving a gradient wind of 60 m.p.h. or more from north-west or north over the North Sea was closely connected with raised water level at the mouth of the Thames, the rise in the water level amounting to 4 feet or more above the height predicted for the astronomical tide. It was, however, also found that such disturbances have a tendency to occur at half-tide and to avoid high tide, thus generally passing without causing flooding in the Thames. Thus, though only one serious flood occurred during fifty years, there had been seventeen cases of raised water at the mouth of the river in twelve years. The real difficulty therefore about anticipating a recurrence of flooding from the causes discussed above lies in the fact that the exact coincidence of the contributing factors occurs so seldom.

The " Further Outlook " in Meteorology

The science of meteorology has advanced to the point where many of the facts of observation and the processes of weather have received what seems to be a satisfactory explanation on physical principles ; numerous details have been made the subject of exact thermodynamical or hydro-dynamical calculation, and mathematical physics plays a not inconsiderable part in the work of the present day professional meteorologist.

The available facts of observation, on the other hand, have continually multiplied, and in all countries we find

increasingly efficient arrangements for collecting and broadcasting the data which go to the preparation of synoptic
charts. It might, therefore, be thought that the time should
be not too distant when the weather of the future should
become a matter of numerical calculation. One bold venture
in this direction has indeed been described in Dr. L. F.
Richardson's *Weather Prediction by Numerical Process*
(Cambridge University Press, 1922) ; but the equations
to be solved in his scheme involve ninety-two different
variables and the amount of labour which would be required
to compute the weather of even a few hours ahead is such
as to render the scheme impracticable. It is thus evident
that, so long as the details have to be handled in their
thousands, forecasting must continue to be a combination
of physical reasoning with practical experience of synoptic
charts.

The Bergen theory of depressions enabled a considerable
advance to be made in the practical handling of daily weather
information in that it rendered possible some degree of
generalization. After studying the reports from individual
stations the meteorologist can frequently analyse his chart
into certain main features and direct his attention to the
movements of great masses of the atmosphere rather than
to the movements of minute elements. Yet even with all
the information now available there is never enough to form
a complete picture. Surface events are represented by
thousands of observations, the upper levels by relatively
few and over vast areas by none. And if reference be made
to the weather chart of Fig. 57 in Chapter XIII it will be
seen that a large area of the Arctic regions is entirely blank.

An organized attempt to obtain data considered necessary
for further research has recently been made on an international scale. It will be recalled that in Chapter XIII
in discussing the question of weather types we referred to
the first International Polar Year, 1882–3, and the series of
detailed daily weather charts which were afterwards constructed from the data collected during that year of special

observation. By international arrangement the year 1932–3 has been observed as the Second International Polar Year. The different nations fitted out expeditions and throughout the year have maintained many observing stations in high latitudes. At these stations, by means of visual observations and by continuously recording instruments, very complete records have been kept.

The results of the First Polar Year were valuable, though at that time the problems to be solved were seen but dimly, the aims of the expeditions were in many cases vague, and the records uncertain. The Second Polar Year has had behind it an elaborate international organization and a clearer idea of the scientific questions to be faced and of the data required for their discussion ; in addition the staffs engaged on the expeditions have consisted largely of men of training and experience in the matters under investigation. Most of the parties have been equipped for obtaining meteorological records, including upper air observations and also records in connection with terrestrial magnetism, the aurora, and atmospheric electricity.

Some years may elapse before all the records can be examined and published, but when this has been done the results will constitute a rich mine of information for regions which hitherto have been little explored ; and many of the blanks on the weather charts of the period 1932–3 can then be filled.

It may well be then that research on the more complete weather picture will disclose new possibilities, render possible greater generalizations, and show important connections, hitherto inapparent or but vaguely suggested, between different groups of terrestrial phenomena.

INDEX

Printed in Great Britain by Stephen Austin & Sons, Limited, Hertford.